FOUNDATION REPAIR SCIENCE

What to Have Done With Your Structural Problem... *and Why*

David Thrasher • Amanda Harrington • Larry Janesky

This book is dedicated to the hard working men and women at Foundation Supportworks dealerships worldwide, who solve foundation structural problems large and small for homeowners and commercial property owners everyday.

FOUNDATION REPAIR SCIENCE ◄
What to Have Done With Your Structural Problem... *and Why*

by David Thrasher, Amanda Harrington and Larry Janesky
design & layout by Scott Clark

Published by:
Foundation Supportworks, Inc.
12330 Cary Circle
Omaha, Nebraska 68128
1-800-281-8545
www.foundationsupportworks.com

ISBN: 978-0-9776457-7-0

2nd Edition
©2010 Foundation Supportworks, Inc. All Rights Reserved.

Table of Contents

How to Use This Book
(A Reader's Guide)

There are nine brief chapters, each dealing with a specific aspect of foundation repair *(see Table of Contents)*. There are many photographs and sidebars to help you understand the ideas. To make things faster, you probably don't have to read chapters that don't apply to you.

For example, if you have a foundation that is settling, you'll need to read chapters 1, 2, 3 and 9 and won't have to read chapters 4 - 8. If your foundation walls are bowing, leaning, or pushing-in, you only need to read chapters 7 - 9. And, if you have slab settlement, problems above your crawl space, or are doing new construction, you can read the chapter specific to those problems.

There are 10 different icons with different meanings:

The subject deals with vertical foundation movement.

The subject deals with horizontal foundation movement.

Apples & Oranges

The two products discussed are very different.

This is important!

Additional information

This subject is very important in getting the results you want.

You will love the results from this!

Beware, don't make this mistake.

This is industry insider information.

Important for the resale value of your home.

Tech Talk

This book is written for the layperson, with the intent to present the topics in a way that are more easily understood. Those who want to, can immerse themselves into the depths of engineering calculations, formulas and vernacular. But, we assume most people just want information in plain English, and so we will spare you the engineer speak in this book.

However, inquisitive minds want to know more. So, we have included some basic technical information in sidebars called 'Tech Talk.' Just who are these 'techies doing the talking?' Let's introduce you to three of the engineers at Foundation Supportworks.

Don Deardorff, P.E., Geotechnical Engineer

Don is an industry veteran, having worked with many other engineers and contractors across the country fixing and stabilizing foundations of homes, buildings, bridges, new structures, etc. – and he's one of the best! Don received his Bachelor of Science degree in Civil Engineering from the University of Missouri-Rolla in 1993, obtained his Master of Science degree in Engineering, and is currently in the dissertation phase of the Ph.D. program.

Jeff Kortan, P.E., Geotechnical Engineer

Prior to becoming involved in the piering and anchoring industry in 2006, **Jeff** served as a consulting engineer for more than 11 years, with varied experience in the areas of site development, landslide stabilization and deep foundations. Jeff graduated from South Dakota State University, receiving a Bachelor of Science degree in Civil Engineering in 1993 and a Master of Science degree in Engineering in 1995.

Kyle Olson, P.E., Structural Engineer

Kyle was a 1996 graduate of North Dakota State University where he earned a Bachelor of Science degree in Civil Engineering. In his 13 years as a project engineer, Kyle designed building structures with a variety of materials including steel, concrete, and timber. Impressive to his resume is his design experience with cranes, mooring systems, and other types of heavy lifting equipment.

▶ *What Does a Geotechnical Engineer Do? Study soils and how structures behave in them! It's important because as you will soon learn in Chapter 1, the soils are the cause of most foundation problems.*

▶ *How About a Structural Engineer? Structural engineers study, well, structures! That's the second part of the equation. How your home (structure) sits on and in the soil!*

Look for these sections!

5

Why We Wrote This Book...

David, Amanda and I teamed up to write this book, and we include the voices of many of us here at Foundation Supportworks. So, yes, we have an interest in its success. But since a foundation repair can be a significant project, you'll need more information than can be provided in a brochure, and the issue deserves more attention than that. When confronted with having a repair project done, most people would want to know what a foremost expert in the field would do to their own home.

It is our intention to give you all the facts and ask all the questions you should be asking when undertaking a foundation repair project. We'll present what is available from our company and others, explore the advantages and disadvantages, and discuss why they are important. We'll look at fixing settling foundations, floor slabs, support columns in crawl spaces, new construction, and bowing or pushed-in foundation walls.

We understand that you're reading this because you are probably shopping for a foundation repair contractor and strategy. While we are stakeholders in a foundation repair company, you are the owner of your home and are the one to make the decision. As with any choice in products and contractors, some are not what they promise, and it may be what you don't know that creates a problem for you if you purchase it. This book is full disclosure of the industry for your consideration.

We hope you get value from this information no matter what you decide to do. We respect that you are the judge.

Larry Janesky

January 2010

In the Beginning...
(An Introduction)

NOTE: This is not a do-it-yourself book because fixing a structural problem at your home is not a do-it-yourself project. It takes too much specialized knowledge, skill, and equipment — and it can be dangerous if you don't know what you're doing.

The purpose of this book is to give you enough information to make an educated decision on what work needs to be done in your home, who to have do it, and why.

What Makes Us Experts?

We work every single day fixing cracked, broken, settling, sinking, bowing, and pushed-in foundations. And, we have a team of coworkers and contributors who have been doing this for many, many years. For example, Greg Thrasher, President of Foundation Supportworks, has been in the foundation business for over 35 years.

This book brings you the collective wisdom of literally hundreds of engineers, tradesmen, contractors, and dealers in the Foundation Supportworks network who have been specializing in the foundation repair business for many years – *and who have been taking responsibility for the results*.

The Foundation Supportworks team includes experts in construction, repair, geotechnical engineering, structural engineering, manufacturing, training, foundation assessment, and installation of repair products. This book is the consensus of all of them – a truly valuable resource if your home's foundation needs repair.

Terms of the Trade

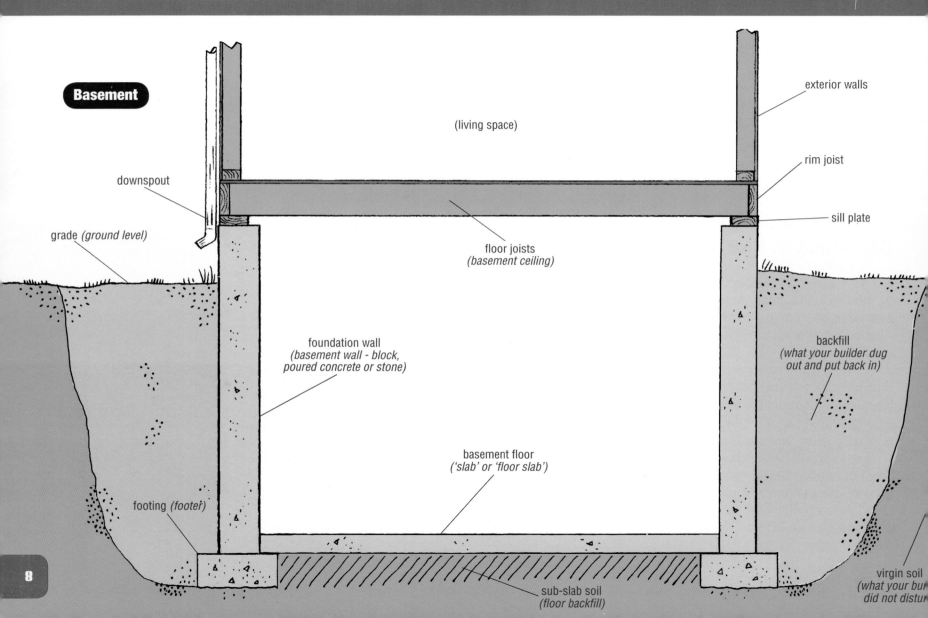

Basement

exterior walls

(living space)

rim joist

downspout

sill plate

grade (ground level)

floor joists
(basement ceiling)

foundation wall
(basement wall - block,
poured concrete or stone)

backfill
(what your builder dug
out and put back in)

basement floor
('slab' or 'floor slab')

footing (footer)

sub-slab soil
(floor backfill)

virgin soil
(what your bui
did not distur

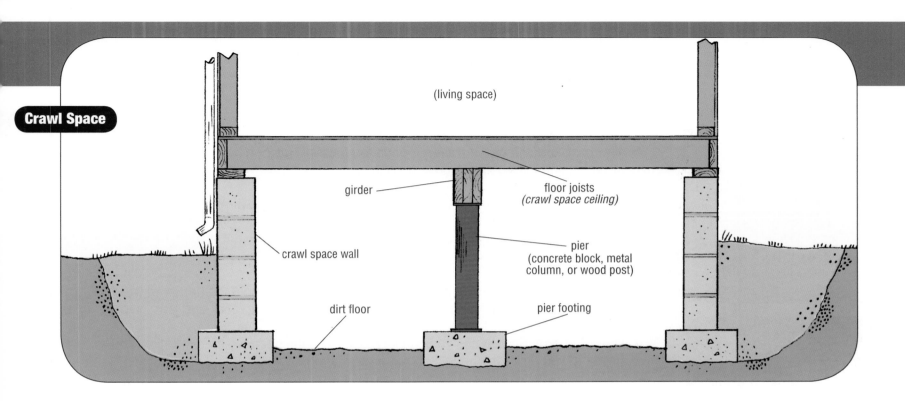

Crawl Space

(living space)

girder

floor joists
(crawl space ceiling)

pier
(concrete block, metal
column, or wood post)

crawl space wall

dirt floor

pier footing

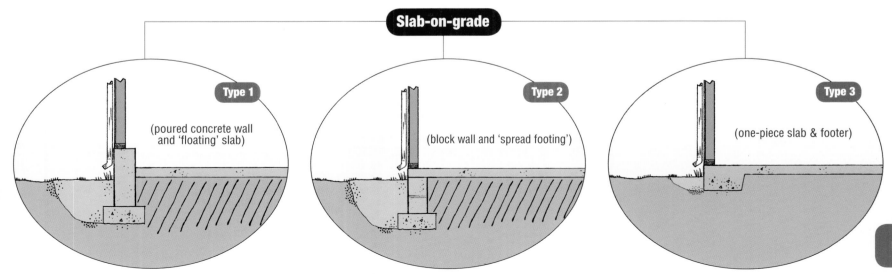

Slab-on-grade

Type 1

(poured concrete wall
and 'floating' slab)

Type 2

(block wall and 'spread footing')

Type 3

(one-piece slab & footer)

Why Should I Fix My Foundation?

This is a good question, with some good reasons, including:

▶ **The problem will get worse**. A foundation problem never gets better on its own – only worse – and as it does, it's going to cost more to fix.

▶ **Resale value**. Who wants to buy a house with a foundation problem? Nobody.

▶ **Appearance**. Foundation problems often cause ugly cracks not only in the foundation itself, but inside the home as well.

▶ **Door and window operation**. As your foundation fails to hold the house where it should be, your house bends and twists – this causes doors and windows to stick and jam, giving you fits.

▶ **Use of space**. Sometimes you can lose use of space because of foundation failure, and that's not what you paid for when you bought your home.

▶ **Safety**. It's unusual, but foundations collapsing, chunks of brick veneer falling off the house, and other serious safety hazards can and have happened.

▶ **Critters like cracks**. Insects and even rodents can get into your home through cracks in your foundation, becoming uninvited house guests.

PRICE REDUCED

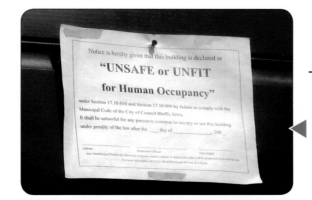

Notice is hereby given that this building is declared as

"UNSAFE or UNFIT
for Human Occupancy"

under Section 17.10.050 and Section 17.10.090 by failure to comply with the Municipal Code of the City of Council Bluffs, Iowa.

It shall be unlawful for any person to continue to occupy or use this building under penalty of the law after the _____ day of _____, 200__.

Ultimately, foundation failure can result in a home being 'unsafe' for living.

You're Going to Pay for It Whether You Fix It or Not.

Consider this: We are all going to sell our homes one day. And when we do, the buyer will hire a home inspector, something few people did 40 years ago, but now everyone does. In addition, when we list our home for sale, there is a disclosure form that sellers must fill out, explaining any defects with the house. You swear and sign to it, and the buyer gets a copy.

So it's simply unavoidable that the buyer is going to know about the foundation problem in your home. Will they say "Aww shucks, don't you worry about that. We'll take the problem off your hands and deal with it ourselves!" Not likely. In fact, they will probably walk away, and go look at the hundreds of other homes for sale out there.

If they do still want your home, they will either make you fix the foundation before they buy it, or they will take the price of the repair off the price of the house. There is no escape.

So whether you get your foundation fixed now and enjoy the peace of mind for you and your family while you live there, or you don't, you are still going to pay for it – and maybe more later as the problem gets worse.

I don't know about you, but if I am going to pay for something whether I get it or not, I'm getting it now. *Make sense?*

Vertical Movement

When the soil under your home shrinks or shifts, then your foundation or parts of it will settle. If the whole foundation settles evenly, you don't notice anything. But usually one part of your home settles more than another part and causes cracks in your foundation. Not good.

Horizontal Movement

When the soil outside of your foundation walls expands, it can cause horizontal movement of your foundation. Because your foundation walls are not supposed to move inward – they crack, bow, lean in, push in, and sometimes slide in. When these walls are supposed to hold up your house and everything and everyone in it, and they aren't even standing up straight anymore – well, that's not good. At all.

Repairing Your Foundation is the 'Green' Alternative

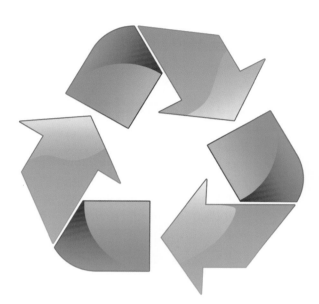

We don't want to be guilty of 'greenwashing' here — when you make up some reasons why your product is environmentally responsible, but it's really a stretch to say as much.

However, here are a few valid points:

Rather than repair your foundation, you could use a very labor intensive and expensive approach — replace it. Not to mention the fact that the new foundation will be sitting on the same unstable soil that caused the original problem, but in replacing your foundation, you would use lots of concrete. Concrete is a very energy intensive material to produce, having to bake limestone for a long time to produce Portland cement.

The products recommended in this book are made from steel. Steel is the most recycled material in the world, and Foundation Supportworks uses recycled steel in its products. We could tell you that our products would be recycled, but it would be hundreds of years before anyone would ever dig them out from around your foundation, so it's pointless.

In any event, it takes less resources to fix what you have than to replace it with new and have the new one meet the same fate.

Your home is your largest investment – financially and emotionally.
Is it resting on a solid foundation?
Don't let your dream home become a nightmare.

CHAPTER 1

What Causes a Foundation to Sink, Settle or Sag?
(The 'Dirt' on Soil)

▷ What Does Your Home Sit On?

At first glance, you might say "the ground!" And, you would be right. When determining what may be causing your home to sink, settle and sag, however, we need to look deeper. What is below the "ground" that you see as you walk out onto your lawn? Soil layers. You home is resting upon many different layers of soil, each with different thicknesses and abilities to hold the weight of your home. They were formed or deposited there thousands and thousands of years ago when the earth was formed. Some layers were carried and deposited by water, some by wind, and some by glaciers. Some layers may have even been put under your home by your home builder, who commonly moves soil around to create flat, buildable lots of land.

Typically, soil layers get stronger with depth. In most locations, you will find a shallow layer near the very surface that is organic, making it easy for plants and other vegetation to grow. Below that top layer, you may find layers of sandy, silty or clayey soils, depending upon where you live and how the soil got there. Deep below these layers is a soil layer of bedrock, which is rock or very stable, dense soil.

Soil layers discovered during the excavation for a new home.

sandy soil loamy soil clayey soil

Not only do different soils have different properties, they also look different.

Moisture and Soil

Different soil types are affected by moisture in different ways. Two very common soil types are sand and clay soils.

SAND — Moisture does not have a big effect on sandy soil. When it rains, the water usually passes through the sand very quickly. When sand gets wet it doesn't expand in size, and when it is dry it doesn't shrink.

CLAY — the problem soil! When clay is wet, it holds onto the water and expands in size. When it is dry, it shrinks.

(moist)   (dry)

These two clay soil samples started out exactly the same – same size, same weight, and same type of clay. The sample on the right was allowed to dry out completely while the sample on the left remained moist. Even the naked eye can see how much the sample on the right reduced in size. Imagine how dramatic this is when clay surrounds your entire home!

The Active Zone!

Important!

The 'active zone' refers to depth of soil beneath the ground surface that is the most affected by changes in moisture as the seasons or climate changes. The active zone may vary from a few feet below grade to more than 30 feet below grade, depending upon what area of the country you live.

ACTIVE ZONE

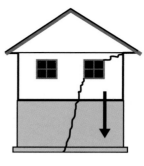

▶ What is Settlement?

Simply stated, settlement is the movement your home experiences when the soil below can no longer support the weight of your home.

Well, the soil used to support my house just fine. So what changed?!

Most likely… the soil changed. There are three common changes in soil that cause settlement:

1. Drying and shrinking of soil *(clay soil is the problem!)*

2. Wetting and softening of soil *(clay strikes again!)*

3. Poorly compacted fill soil

1. Drying and shrinking of soil

• **Drought**. After many months or years of drought, clay soil dries out. And, as we know, when clay dries, it shrinks. As the amount of soil around your house shrinks in size, it creates an empty space for your home to settle into.

• **Maturing trees**. Did you know that the root system of a tree is often two times the size of the tree canopy? This means, a tree with branches that extend over your home, most likely has roots that extend under your home, drawing valuable moisture from the soil. When the soil dries out… you know the drill!

Beware of the heave!
Heave is the opposite of settlement, but can show similar signs. For more information about heave, see page 48.

CAUTION

2. *Wetting and softening of soil*

• **Heavy rain & flood conditions**. As clay soil gets wet, it holds on to the water and becomes very soft. This soft soil can be weak, causing the home to shift or 'sink' down into it. In some ways, it is similar to when you step in mud and your foot 'squishes' into the soil

• **Poor drainage.** If water is allowed to stand or pond next to your home, the soil will absorb the water and again, weaken the soil.

C1

3. *Poorly compacted fill soil*

A common practice when building a new home involves removing soil from hilltops and placing it in valleys to create flat, buildable lots. If this fill soil is not compacted well, it will begin to compress under the weight of the new home, causing settlement.

Did You Know...
*Settlement is often associated with older homes, but a recent article from **Consumer Reports** shows that an alarming 15% of new homes have structural problems. These problems generally have two causes: poor construction or homes built on poorly compacted fill soils.*

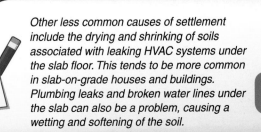

Side Note

Other less common causes of settlement include the drying and shrinking of soils associated with leaking HVAC systems under the slab floor. This tends to be more common in slab-on-grade houses and buildings. Plumbing leaks and broken water lines under the slab can also be a problem, causing a wetting and softening of the soil.

19

In regions of the southeast United States, natural sinkholes are a common problem. Sinkholes are holes or depressions in the soil caused by dissolving or eroding of the underlying limestone. As groundwater moves through limestone beneath the earth's surface, large voids and cavities are created. As water continues to move through the cavity, more and more of the limestone is eroded. This process continues until soil is exposed at the ceiling of the cavity. When this soil collapses into the cavity, a sinkhole is formed. Although scary, homes above sinkholes can be stabilized. *Read on!*

Mother Nature:
Mother Knows Best!

 Q: *I haven't seen anything change in my home recently. Don't you think my home is 'done' settling?*

A: *We are dealing with Mother Nature. The constant cycle of wet and dry periods indicates that settlement in a home may never be over.*

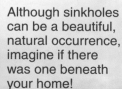

Although sinkholes can be a beautiful, natural occurrence, imagine if there was one beneath your home!

And so the cycles continue...

The ONLY way to know settlement is 'done' is to <u>FIX</u> the problem!

SINK SETTLE SAG

► Signs *Outside* Your Home

• Stair-Step Cracking

Stair-step cracking is often a tell-tale sign of foundation settlement and is very common in brick and concrete block walls. As your home continues to settle further, vertical cracks may widen, indicating that the wall is rotating outward.

• Chimneys

One of the more scary and dramatic signs of settlement is a chimney separating away from the rest of the home. Sometimes chimneys are built on a foundation that is not connected to the rest of the home, making it even more at risk of settlement.

Side Note

As vertical cracks form and the wall or corner of the house begins to rotate, you will typically see cracks that are wider at the top than at the bottom.

• *Clues from Doors and Windows*

Whenever an opening is cut or created in a wall, such as a door or window, it becomes the weakest point of the wall. Because of this, doors and windows often display the first signs of settlement. **Three common observations include:** 1) Doors and windows out of square, 2) Cracks extending from the corners of doors or windows, and 3) The separation of a door or window from the framing or exterior finish.

Have you noticed newer caulking around exterior doors or windows? This is a common homeowner fix to the damages caused by foundation settlement.

Side Note

You and your neighbor share soil. If your neighbor is experiencing problems, chances are, you will too.

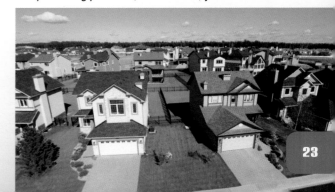

▶ Should I Hide the Problem or Fix It?

Hiding the problem by patching over drywall cracks or tuck-pointing cracks in brick or block are only band-aid fixes. The real problem still exists and hasn't been solved. The cracks will re-appear, more repairs will need to be made, and soon you will have a patch over a patch over a patch. Additionally, attempts to fill or seal drywall or mortar cracks are easy to identify due to variances in finish or workmanship. When tuck-pointing brick veneer, it is especially difficult to match original mortar colors. So, are you really hiding anything? Plus, you have to disclose the problem anyway if you ever plan to sell the house.

Patching cracks in exterior bricks (or tuck-pointing) only cosmetically (and temporarily) hide the problem.

Signs *Inside* Your Home

Many of the signs you can see on the outside of your home are similar to the ones inside your basement. Stair-step cracks, for example, may be seen in a basement built from concrete block. In a basement constructed of poured foundation walls, vertical cracks are more common.

Cracks in your concrete floor slab can signal foundation settlement, but may also be a sign that the slab alone has settled. For more information on slab settlement, turn to chapter four!

Be careful not to assume that a crack in your foundation is merely a shrinkage crack. Shrinkage cracks tend to be very small, 'hairline' cracks (usually 1/16" wide or less). They generally occur near the center of a span and maintain a consistent width for the length of the crack.

CAUTION

Cracks in your concrete floor are an indication of slab settlement.

Looking Around Upstairs

Drywall Cracks – Cracks in drywall throughout the house are a good indicator of settlement, and may be more obvious in the uppermost levels of your house. The following signs are common:

- Drywall cracks off of the corners of doors and windows
- Cracks that follow drywall seams
- Drywall tape buckling, pulling or ripping

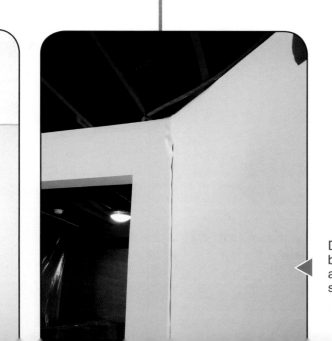

Drywall cracks (TOP), buckling drywall tape (LEFT), and cracks along drywall seams (FAR LEFT).

Doors and Windows – Again, observing what is happening around doors and windows is important. Ask yourself this:

- When I put a level across the top of the door or window frame, is it level?

- Do any of my doors or windows 'stick' when I try to open or close them?

- Have I planed across the top of a door to make it open and close more easily? Is there evidence that a previous homeowner has done this?

- Have I had to move or replace locking or latching mechanisms on doors? Is there evidence that a previous homeowner has done this?

If you answered 'yes' to any of these questions, chances are, you have a foundation settlement problem!

Wait a Minute!

The cracks in my home aren't <u>THIS</u> bad!

<u>Remember</u> – big cracks once started as small cracks...

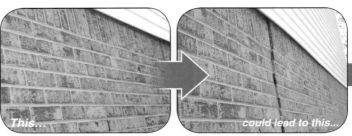

This...   could lead to this...

How long will *you* wait to fix the problem?

27

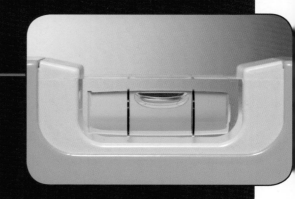

CHAPTER 3

Solutions to Foundation Settlement

*On the <u>Level</u>: What Works and Doesn't Work
in Solving Your Foundation Settlement Problem*

Apples & Oranges

CAUTION

▶ Fixing It!

The subtitle of this book is *'What to Have Done With Your Structural Problem… and Why.'* As with anything, there are a variety of options for fixing your foundation, some more effective than others. Shopping for a solution to your foundation settlement problem is serious business. You need a solution from a trustworthy contractor who will solve your problem…permanently. Unfortunately, the wide variety of options can create confusion, so let's talk about some solutions to beware of.

Total Foundation Replacement

What is it? With total foundation replacement, the soil is first excavated from around your foundation walls. Then, the house is jacked up and the slab floor and foundation walls are removed. Finally, the foundation is rebuilt and the soil is replaced.

Why might people choose this? If my foundation is broken, it seems logical to replace it with a new one rather than to repair the existing one.

Why this doesn't work. Not only is replacement extremely disruptive and expensive, the real problem is that it doesn't address the issue. The foundation isn't the problem; the soil is the problem *(see chapter 1)*. You've simply built a new foundation in the same troublesome soil, so you can expect that your new foundation will 'break' just like the old one!

Concrete Underpinning

What is it? After soil is excavated from around the foundation, larger concrete footings are poured beneath the existing footings. Once the concrete has cured, the soil is backfilled.

Why might people choose this? If a footing is designed to carry the weight of the home, then a bigger footing should be better...right?! Contractors who know just a little may not know any other way.

Why this doesn't work. Most of the time, concrete underpinning does not extend past the 'active zone' and beyond the troubled soils. In other words, the soil beneath these newly beefed-up footings may still be moving, causing the home above to continue to move. Additionally, concrete shrinks as it cures, potentially creating small gaps between the new footing and the old one. Open gaps beneath a home are never a good thing.

When concrete underpinning is used as a solution and the problem continues, it is MUCH more expensive to repair as all of the added concrete will need to be removed and resupported by a new, more substantial foundation system.

Underpinning didn't work on these houses. Eventually the homeowner had to invest in a different solution that would fix the problem permanently.

Concrete Piers

What is it? Short, blunt concrete cylinders are pushed into the soil on top of one another and are held together by a wire. Shims are then placed on top of the uppermost concrete cylinder, and the soil is backfilled.

Why might people choose this? Concrete seems like a pretty strong material, so it must work, right?!

Why this doesn't work. The blunt concrete cylinders are wide in diameter *(about six to eight inches)*, making it difficult to push the sections deep into the ground and past the troubled soil. There is also nothing to guide the direction of the pier, so they may not be installed straight. Finally, although concrete is a strong material, we've all seen concrete crack and break under pressure and during changes in temperature. Just take a look at all of the cracks in concrete streets and parking lots! If concrete piers were a great idea, all manufacturers of foundation repair products would offer them. Instead, only a few companies struggle with this approach.

Do you want this holding up your greatest investment? ▶

▶ Fixing It!

*Now let's talk about some solutions that **DO** work...*

▶ Steel Push *(or Resistance)* Piers

What is it? Push piers, sometimes known as resistance piers, are made of steel and are driven deep into the soil to bedrock or other stable soil layer. Push piers can be installed from the exterior or interior of your home and can provide an opportunity to lift your home back toward its original position, oftentimes closing cracks and improving the operation of doors and windows.

How does it work? First, soil is removed from the area where the pier will be driven. A heavy-duty steel bracket is then installed below and against your foundation's footing. Rugged, steel pier sections are hydraulically driven through the bracket to bedrock or a stable soil layer. Next, the weight of the home is transferred through the piers to competent soil below, and a lift can be attempted to bring the home back toward its original position. Once the homeowner and installing contractor are satisfied with the stabilization or amount of lift, the soil can be backfilled and the home is permanently stabilized in its new position.

Steel push piers can be installed from the inside of your home. The completed installation is neat and clean and will be completely covered by carpet or other floor covering.

When to use it. Because push piers are driven all the way to bedrock or a stable soil layer, push piers are often the least risky solution when local soil conditions are unknown. If your goals are the following, push piers are a good choice:

- Best opportunity to lift the home back toward its original position.
- Minimal disturbance from installation.
- Quick installation compared to other solutions.
- Restore property value.
- *__Problem solved once and for all!__*

When NOT to use it. When installing piers on lighter structures such as stoops or decks, a solution such as a helical pier may be more effective than a push pier because the structure may not be heavy enough to drive push piers to sufficient depth.

▶ Push Piers: *Why Foundation Supportworks' Are the Best*

Important!

You'll Love This!

As with any family of products, there are good, better, and best. And when you are talking about fixing your home, you may as well go with the best. When we say best, we mean the strongest. The **FSI** *(Foundation Supportworks, Inc.)* **Push Pier** features a patent-pending external sleeve which strengthens the pier system directly below the bracket (which is the most critical location). The external sleeve strengthens this area and prevents the kinking, buckling, and rotating commonly seen with other push pier systems

And, by the way, the *best* doesn't cost more than the good or better models.

TECH TALK

Apples & Oranges

Important!

INSIDER INFORMATION

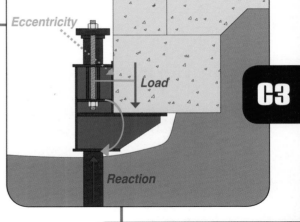

Beware of contractors who tout the strength and capacity of their system's bracket. The bracket is only one piece of the puzzle – you need to be aware of all the components and how they contribute to the system's capacity. Generally speaking, all push pier systems are installed in a similar way. Your foundation's footing is exposed, a bracket is secured to the footing, and pier tubes are driven through the bracket to load bearing strata. In any repair application, such as your home, piers are driven adjacent to the foundation. This affect is what we engineers call *eccentricity*.

Because of this eccentricity, all pier systems see the greatest levels of bending stress directly below the bottom of the bracket. So the question is, how do we strengthen our piering system to resist these forces effectively?

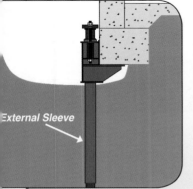

One approach would be to use a thicker pier tube. While this may sound like a good idea, it is not an economical solution. The problem with this approach is that extra steel is then added to the entire length of the pier. Since the added steel is only required directly below the bracket, the substantial extra steel costs are essentially wasted on the rest of the pier.

A second and very common approach is to try and add extra reinforcing inside the tube after the pier has been driven. With the greatest forces exerted during the driving operation, weaker systems tend to bend and kink, making it impossible to insert the extra reinforcing.

Once this bending and kinking occurs, the strength and effectiveness of the pier system is compromised. No matter how strong a bracket is claimed to be, many weaker systems fail due to the bending forces beneath the bracket.

Foundation Supportworks has developed a unique and revolutionary solution to this problem – *the external sleeve*. The Foundation Supportworks external sleeve is driven at the very beginning of the pier installation. Once the external sleeve is in place, all other pier tubes are driven through it. What are the advantages of this approach? The extra steel is added where it needs to be, right beneath the foundation bracket. This is a very efficient use of the steel. The sleeve resists bending forces as the pier tubes are pushed through it. This not only guides the angle at which the pier is being installed, but also increases the strength of the entire pier system dramatically.

The true determination of the strength and effectiveness of a push pier lies in understanding the installation process and how all the forces travel through the pier system. Claims of bracket capacity and strength only tell a part of the story. Knowing the capacity of the entire system as a whole is the surest way to know you are making the right choice when selecting a system.

This pier is bending to the point where the galvanizing is being scraped off the outside of the tube. There is no way a reinforcing tube will fit in this pier after the pier has been driven.

External Sleeve

Other System (kinked & failed)

Foundation Supportworks (sleeve resists bending)

Some foundation contractors claim to have very strong pier brackets. But as you can see in these photos, a strong bracket alone can't prevent these pier systems from bending and kinking. These homeowners were hoping for a permanent solution to their foundation settlement problem.

Can you imagine their disappointment?

▶ Fixing It!

More solutions that work...

▶ Helical Piers

What is it? A helical pier is another steel piering system. The first section that is advanced into the ground has one or more bearing plates or helical blades welded to the shaft. Additional sections, or extensions, do not have bearing plates and are used to extend the pier to the necessary installation depth. Helical piers can be installed from the exterior or interior of your home and provide an opportunity to lift your home back toward its original position. Helical piers can also be effective at closing cracks caused by settlement and improving the operation of doors and windows.

How does it work? First, soil is removed from the area where the helical pier will be installed. Helical pier sections are mechanically 'screwed' into the soil. Once proper depths and capacities are achieved, heavy-duty steel foundation brackets are positioned below and against the footing. The weight of the home is then transferred through the helical piers to deep, competent soils. Lifting the home back toward its original position is attempted, and the soil around the installation is then replaced.

When to use it. With knowledge of local soil conditions, helical piers can be an ideal solution because the installing contractor will know exactly how deep to install the piers to reach a stable soil layer that can support your home. If your goals are the following, helical piers are a good choice:

- Attempt to lift the home back toward its original position.

- Stabilize lighter structures that have settled, such as decks or stoops.

- Minimal disturbance from installation.

- Quick installation compared to other solutions.

- Restore property value.

- ***Problem solved once and for all!***

When NOT to use it. Less experienced helical pier installers may not advance the pier deep enough if a stiff soil layer is encountered near the surface, which may be above the deeper problematic soil layer.

▶ Helical Piers: *Why Foundation Supportworks' Are the Best*

It's the little things that make a big difference when comparing Foundation Supportworks helical pier system vs. helical pier systems from other manufacturers. The **International Code Council (ICC)** is the association responsible for developing the codes and standards used to construct residential and commercial buildings. The ICC has established specific criteria for evaluating helical piers, but unfortunately not all manufacturers follow it.

An example of how some manufacturers do not follow the ICC criteria is how they manufacture their helix bearing plates. Some nonconforming manufacturers' blades have a more 'duckbill' appearance rather than a true helix shape. The result? The helical pier acts like an auger, churning up and disturbing the soil as it is installed.

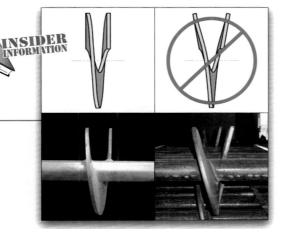

Correct   **Incorrect**

Helical sections are connected to one another by a coupler. This is another area where most manufacturers can get a little sloppy. If the product is not manufactured to very strict tolerances that allow end-to-end contact between the pier sections, the weight of the structure is forced to travel through welds and bolts at the pier couplers, rather than through the pier shafts themselves.

FSI helical pier systems are designed according to the criteria outlined by the ICC and are manufactured with the strictest tolerances in the industry. That means — it's tested, it's strong, and it will perform as promised. Put simply, they are the best.

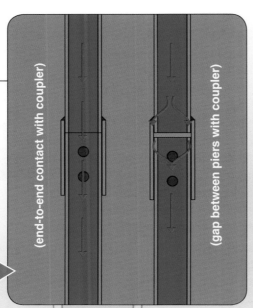

A comparison of weight transfer by end-to-end contact versus bolt contact pier 'couplers' (connectors).

(end-to-end contact with coupler)

(gap between piers with coupler)

Square Shaft vs. Round Shaft Helical Piers

C3

A round shaft helical pier by any other name just isn't the same… When some contractors talk about installing helical piers, their solution is a square shaft helical pier rather than a round shaft helical pier. Round shaft, rather than square shaft helical piers, should be used to support a home's settling foundation for the following reasons:

• Square shaft helical piers use a socket and pin coupling which results in deviations from straightness, introduces additional eccentricity to the system, and increases buckling potential.

• The steel area for a section of round shaft is located outward from the center of the shaft, therefore creating a higher resistance to bending.

• Round shafts usually have a higher installation torque rating, meaning more force can be applied while the product is being installed. Higher installation torque generally correlates to higher soil capacities.

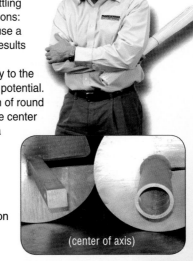

(center of axis)

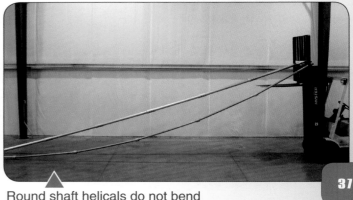

Round shaft helicals do not bend like their square shaft counterparts!

Lifespan of Black Steel

With steel piering systems there is a great debate about whether the product can be installed with black, uncoated steel, or if it's necessary to galvanize the steel for greater corrosion resistance. There are many factors that can go into the argument and many site-specific variables that can influence the decision. *But here are some facts:*

1. Everything degrades over time and is consumed by Mother Earth.

2. In order for corrosion to occur, three things must be present: water, oxygen, and corrosive material.

3. Deep in the ground, a steel pier may encounter water, but will encounter very little oxygen. Near the surface, steel is more likely to be exposed to both. Therefore, the deeper the steel is, the slower the corrosion process.

   a. *It's sort of like a ship that has sunk to the bottom of the ocean. It takes a VERY long time for the steel to corrode due to the lack of oxygen.*

4. Galvanizing does protect and extend the life of steel.

5. Foundation Supportworks designs and analyzes our products keeping in mind corrosion loss rates provided by the International Code Council. All FSI products can be installed with either black or galvanized steel, depending on the site-specific conditions and desires of the home owner.

6. Either way, black or galvanized steel will likely outlast the components used to build the home itself.

black steel

galvanized steel

Side Note

Pier Application Chart

Choose the Right System for <u>YOU</u> Based on Your Situation and Goals

Condition \ Solution ▶	Removal & Replacement	Concrete Underpinning	Concrete Piers	Helical Piers	Push Piers
New Construction of Home or Addition	N/A	N/A	✗	✓	✗
Can Be Installed from Home's Interior	N/A	✗	✓	✓	✓
Installation Usually Completed in Less Than One Week	✗	✗	✓	✓	✓
Lowest Risk When Local Soil Information is Unknown	✗	✗	✗	✗	✓
Stabilize Light Structures Such as Decks or Stoops	✓	✓	✗	✓	✗
Limited Disturbance to Lawn & Landscaping	✗	✗	✓	✓	✓
Solution Extends Past Troubled Soils	✗	✗	✗	✓	✓
Permanently Stabilize Foundation Without Maintenance	✗	✗	✗	✓	✓
Ability to Lift Home Back to Level	✗	✗	✓	✓	✓

CASE STUDY

Product: Model 288 Push Piers
Project: Residence
Location: Charring Cross, Ontario
Date: December 2009

Piers installed and lift in process.

PROBLEM

The residence was built in 1975 in a rural setting in the SW Ontario countryside. In 1995, the homeowners decided to add living space to the rear of the main structure. The exterior of the addition was constructed of brick and was supported by a poured concrete foundation. Approximately thirteen years after construction, the homeowners began to notice signs of settlement on the addition, such as windows becoming difficult to open and close, and both interior and exterior cracking. The addition appeared to have settled over 1.5 inches away from the rest of the home.

Settlement crack **BEFORE**.

SOLUTION

Advanced Basement Systems installed a total of eleven (11) Foundation Supportworks Model 288 Push Piers along the perimeter of the addition to remedy the problem. Due to the architectural design of the addition, the two side walls supported most of the weight of the structure. Therefore, three piers were installed on the rear wall and four piers were installed on each of the two side walls. The piers were installed to ultimate capacities of over 40,000 pounds, effectively stabilizing the home's foundation.

Settlement crack **AFTER**.

RESULTS

The installation by Advanced Basement Systems was extremely effective in not only stabilizing the structure, but also lifting the foundation back to its original position. The homeowners were amazed that the Advanced crews were able to close cracks and displacement gaps between the foundation and the brick. On the inside of the structure, the wood base-boards and flooring were raised back to their original positions and windows opened and closed much easier. The customer was 'extremely pleased' with the results as well as the efficiency and cleanliness of the Advanced Basement Systems crew.

Settlement crack **BEFORE**.

40

PROJECT SUMMARY

Installing Contractor: Advanced Basement Systems, Chatham, ON
Products Installed: (11) Foundation Supportworks Model 288 Push Piers

Settlement crack **AFTER**.

One of several cracks in the home's foundation.

Removal of failed bottle jacks and large concrete footing put in place by the first repair contractor.

Secondary footing removed and helical piers installed.

Helical piers installed; foundation stabilized and leveled prior to backfilling.

Product: Model 288 Helical Piers
Project: Residence
Location: Lima, Ohio
Date: April 2009

CASE STUDY

PROBLEM

The home is a wood-framed structure that was originally built in 1957, with an addition added in 1997. Almost immediately following construction of the new addition, the homeowner observed warning signs of foundation settlement, including drywall cracks, doors and windows that did not fully open or close, and cracks in the foundation walls. In 2004 a contractor was hired to support the house and then pour large concrete footings beneath the existing foundation. This is a fairly common practice to provide deeper and larger footings, but is often ineffective since the new concrete is bearing on the same weak soil. The decision proved to be a costly mistake as the foundation settlement continued almost immediately following the repair.

SOLUTION

J&D Basement Systems replaced the ineffective concrete footings with nine (9) Foundation Supportworks Model 288 Helical Piers to permanently stabilize the foundation. The piers were advanced to depths of over 12 feet and to estimated ultimate capacities of over 47,000 pounds. L-shaped foundation support brackets were then positioned below and against the footings and hydraulic cylinders were used to lift the foundation back toward a level position. The helical piers effectively stabilized the foundation and restored value to the home. The homeowner now has peace of mind knowing that the foundation was fixed properly with the added assurance of a 25 year warranty.

TESTIMONIAL

"I have had these structural issues with my home for many years and have tried different ways to fix the problems. The J&D inspector took time to analyze the issues and develop a cost effective and efficient way to correct the problem once and for all. I am impressed with the results and am confident of their long term effects." – Homeowner

PROJECT SUMMARY

Installing Contractor: J&D Basement Systems – Northwest • Elida, OH
Products Installed: (9) Foundation Supportworks Model 288 Helical Piers, 8/10 Lead Section

What a Difference!

The installation of push piers and helical piers can close cracks, improve the operation of doors and windows, restore property value, but most importantly, give you the peace of mind knowing the problem is solved once and for all!

before

after

before

after

before

after

before

after

CHAPTER 4

Concrete Floor Slab: Settlement and Solutions
What to Do When Your Concrete Slab Floor is Cracked and Sinking

▶ What Causes a Concrete Floor Slab to Settle?

As we discussed in Chapter 2, cracks in a floor slab can indicate a foundation settlement problem. But be careful! Sometimes those cracks can be misleading. It is possible that while the foundation remains stable and in place, the floor slab alone is settling. Or, the slab cracks can be the result of a problem called heave, which we'll cover later in this chapter. If either of these are the problem, the piering systems we talked about in Chapter 3 will not solve it.

Slab settlement is most common in slab-on-grade homes and buildings where the floor slab is closer to the ground surface and therefore more influenced by the soil in the 'active zone'. Slab settlement usually occurs because of one of the following reasons:

① Drying and shrinking of the soil under the slab.

Clay soil strikes again! Ductwork for Heating, Ventilating, and Air Conditioning (HVAC) systems may be installed beneath the floor slab. Over time, the ductwork can leak, and the leaking air can dry out the soil. As this soil dries and shrinks, gaps form under the floor slab creating a void. Because the soil no longer supports the floor slab, the floor begins to crack and sink into the void.

② Washout of soil under the slab.

This is usually caused by plumbing leaks. If the plumbing leak is severe and there is a path for the water to flow, it can wash the soil out from under the slab, creating a void. Once again, the floor slab no longer has the soil supporting it and begins to crack and sink into the void.

③ Poor compaction of fill soil.

During construction of a new home, layers of soil are commonly moved around or spread out to get to the desired grade level. When the home is built, footings may be deepened to extend below weak fill soils. The slab, however, remains on the fill soils. If the fill was poorly compacted, the fill soil compresses and settles, and a void is created under the slab. Then the slab cracks, breaks, and settles into the void.

Erosion *(similar to this)* can occur under your slab after a major plumbing leak.

▶ *Signs of Slab Settlement*

- Cracks in the concrete floor, oftentimes creating dangerous trip hazards.

- Floors dropping and separating from walls, forming a gap between the floor and the wall.

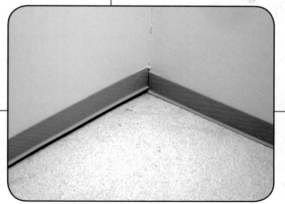

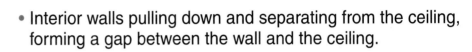

- Interior walls pulling down and separating from the ceiling, forming a gap between the wall and the ceiling.

- Walls pulling away from other, adjacent walls.

- Interior wall cracks, commonly off the corners of interior doors.

CAUTION

Beware of Heave!

Some contractors who have not been educated on the signs of heave can easily misread the cracks in your home and suggest the wrong solution. Heave is the opposite of settlement, but can show similar signs.

So what is heave? Heave is the upward movement of a foundation or slab caused by expanding or swelling of the underlying clay soils due to an increase in moisture. Heave is more common for slabs than foundations since the weight of the home on the foundation may partially or fully affect the swell force. Heave typically occurs within the first few years after new construction unless there are long periods of drought.

What causes heave? When a hole is dug for a new home, the upper layers of soil may be dry. Or, sometimes the hole is allowed to remain open and the soil dries out. After the home is built, moisture contents of dry soils below interior slabs will naturally increase. As these moisture levels increase, the clay soil expands, putting pressure on the floor slab. The floor slab is pushed upward. Interior partition walls are also lifted, which causes cracking in drywall.

What are the tell-tale signs of heave? To the untrained eye, it may appear that the exterior walls are going down, rather than the center going up. You will generally see no cracking to outside foundation walls but will instead see cracking in interior partition walls and floors. Cracks in the floor slab caused by heave are unique – multiple cracks come together to a point or form an enclosed loop where the heave is the greatest.

The moral of the story?

Piering systems cannot control heave after the fact. If a contractor comes into your home and suggests that a piering system can solve it – <u>BEWARE</u>! You may be meeting with a contractor who knows just a little. The investment of a piering system will not give you the return you are hoping for.

▶ Fixing a Settling Floor Slab

What <u>NOT</u> to Have Done... and Why

Concrete Slab Replacement

What is it? All home furnishings, floor coverings and interior partition walls must first be removed. Then a jackhammer is used to break the existing floor slab into small pieces. All of those small pieces must be removed from the home by hand. Then a new floor is poured and allowed to cure for at least two weeks. Then interior partition walls can be re-built, floor coverings re-installed, and home furnishings brought back in.

Why might people choose this? If my floor slab is broken, it seems logical to replace it with a new one rather than to repair the existing one.

Why this doesn't work. This solution is obviously disruptive and expensive, but the real problem is that it doesn't address the issue. The floor isn't the problem; the soil is the problem (just a warning…this is going to be a common theme on what NOT to have done…and why)! You've poured a new floor slab over same troublesome soil, so you can expect that your new floor will "break" just like the old one.

Mudjacking

What is it? A series of holes are drilled throughout your concrete floor, and a high-pressure grout is pumped beneath the slab to fill in the void below.

Why might people choose this? It fills in the void below the slab, so my floor slab shouldn't settle any further.

Why this doesn't work. The high-pressure grout is messy, spewing grout out of other holes and cracks in the slab. The grout alone may not be able to lift heavy partition walls sitting on top of the slab back to their original, level position. Or, if the slab does lift, it may be difficult to control and not lift evenly. But, most importantly, the solution is not permanent. Even with the voids filled, the soil below will continue to settle beneath the slab, and you'll have to call in a contractor to mudjack again and again and again *(or call in a contractor who uses a solution that will fix the problem once and for all)*.

Re-leveling Grout on Top of the Slab

What is it? After the floor coverings are removed, the floor is prepped so grout is able to bond to the slab surface. A self-leveling grout is poured over the surface of the slab, where it begins to fill in the lowest portion of the floor to develop a level surface. After the grout is allowed to cure for several days, the floor coverings can be replaced.

Why might people choose this? I just want a level floor again, so this seems to make sense.

Why this doesn't work. If the floor wasn't prepared properly, the grout may not bond well to the surface of the slab and it may break off in chunks. Additionally, the grout adds weight to the slab, potentially making the situation worse by causing further settlement. And, like the last two options, the real problem, the soil, isn't addressed. Do we sound like a broken record yet?!

► Fixing a Settling Floor Slab

What TO Have Done... and Why

Before

After

Deep-driven Slab Piers

What is it? Slab piers are steel piers which are driven or advanced deep below your floor slab to a stable soil layer. These piers are driven or advanced deep into the ground, past any troubled soil, so that your slab is supported by a strong, competent material. There are two types of slab piers: hydraulically-driven slab piers and helical slab piers. Both types can be effective, and selecting one over the other depends on your unique situation and the efficiency of the contractor who is installing them. Both types of slab piers use small installation equipment, so installations can be completed in tight-access areas such as bathrooms or laundry rooms. Slab piers also provide an opportunity to lift your concrete slab back to its original position, oftentimes closing cracks and eliminating trip hazards.

How Does It Work? The process for installing hydraulically-driven slab piers and helical slab piers is very similar. In both cases, the first step is to core a small hole in the concrete floor. If installing hydraulically-driven slab piers, a slab bracket is then positioned beneath the concrete slab and steel piers are hydraulically driven through the bracket to deep, competent soils. If installing helical slab piers, helical pier sections are first advanced deep into the soil and then the slab bracket is positioned beneath the concrete slab. For both systems, the next step is to transfer the weight of the concrete slab through the piers to the deep, stable soil. Then, a lift can be attempted to bring the slab and interior partition walls back to their original position. Grout is then carefully pumped at a low pressure under the slab to fill the void created by the soil settlement and slab lifting process. Finally, concrete is placed back in the cored holes, and the floor is permanently stabilized in its new position.

Each pier is hydraulically driven.

C4

When to use it. Other than if the floor slab is extremely thin, or if cracking is extensive, there really isn't a situation when you *wouldn't* use slab piers. Here are just some of the advantages:

- Best opportunity to lift the slab and interior partition walls back toward their original position.

- Non-disruptive and non-invasive installation – small holes are cored in the slab and then re-filled after installation.

- Reduces trip hazards.

- Restores property value.

- ***Problem solved once and for all!***

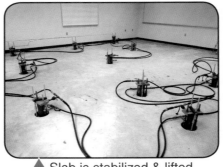
Slab is stabilized & lifted.

Cored holes are filled.

▶ Slab Piers: *Why Foundation Supportworks' Are the Best*

Important!

You'll **Love** This!

Because the Foundation Supportworks slab pier system will be completely hidden after installation, you'll never see one of the most unique aspects of it – the bracket! The challenge in designing a bracket for a slab pier system is that you have to balance the size of the bracket with the size of the hole that has been cored in the floor. In order to keep the cored hole as small as possible, you must limit the size of the bracket. Or do you? Foundation Supportworks has developed a unique bracket which consists of three plates that are individually placed into the hole, but are easily assembled as one larger unit once they are under the slab. Why does this matter? The larger the bracket, the more surface area it covers, allowing for a more even distribution or spread of the load. Other slab pier systems use one single plate as the bracket, limited by the size of the cored hole. As a result, it's more likely to see cracks in the floor slab from the pressure being put on that one single, small bracket.

CASE STUDY

Product: Model 288 Slab Piers
Project: Housing Authority of Russellville
Location: Russellville, KY
Date: July 2009

Russellville Housing Authority duplexes were constructed in the 1960's.

CHALLENGE

The Russellville Housing Authority was established in the late 1950's. In the early 1960's they began constructing one-story, slab-on-grade duplexes with masonry block walls and brick veneer. Fill soil was placed over the original sloping ground surface to level the area for the construction of some of the first units. The floor slab of the unit in question rested on a layer of this fill soil. Over the years, the floor slab settled as the loosely-compacted fill soils consolidated. Differential settlements ranged from one to three inches, causing gaps to form between the floor and the base trim, interior doors to stick within racked door frames, and cabinets, countertops, plumbing fixtures, and the bathtub to settle and pull away from walls. The floor slab settlement even caused an exterior foundation wall to rotate outward. The Housing Authority compensated for the settlement over the years by adjusting or adding base trim and adjusting the doors and cabinets.

Slab settlement was severe and ranged from one to three inches.

SOLUTION

The original project specification called for 21 interior helical slab piers to stabilize and then lift the settled slab areas of one of the duplex units. Two additional helical foundation support piers were required to stabilize the exterior footing. Due to the rocky soil conditions and the limited working space within the unit, hydraulically-driven slab piers and foundation piers were selected as a more favorable alternative. Twenty-one (21) slab piers were installed in a grid pattern spacing of about 5 feet. The slab piers were driven individually to depths ranging from 8 to 12 feet, and each to a force of at least 9,000 pounds. The two exterior foundation piers were driven to over 45,000 pounds of force. The interior slab and non-load bearing interior walls were lifted back toward a level position and the outside corner and foundation was lifted approximately one-quarter inch. In all, 23 piers were installed in 6 days, which allowed the renovation project to proceed on schedule.

The slab piers were driven individually to competent strata using hydraulic equipment.

PROJECT SUMMARY

Certified Installer: Frontier Basement Systems
Products Installed: (21) Foundation Supportworks Model 288 Slab Piers, (2) Foundation Supportworks Model 288 Push Piers

Hydraulic lift cylinders were attached and the slabs and interior non-load bearing walls were lifted back to a level position.

Slab Pier Application Chart

Choose the Right System for <u>YOU</u> Based on Your Situation and Goals

Condition \ Solution ▶	Removal & Replacement	Mudjacking	Re-leveling Grout	Slab Piers
Installation Usually Completed in Less Than One Week	✗	✓	✓	✓
Minimal Disturbance to Interior Finishes (Walls)	✗	✓	✗	✓
No Waiting for Concrete to Cure	✗	✗	✗	✓
Effective When Slab Floor is Very Thin	✓	✗	✓	✗
Solution Extends Past Troubled Soils	✗	✗	✗	✓
Permanently Stabilize Slab Without Maintenance	✗	✗	✗	✓
Ability to Lift Slab and Interior Partition Walls Back to Level	✗	✓	✗	✓

Before & After

What a Difference!

C4

The installation of slab piers can close cracks, eliminate dangerous trip hazards, restore property value, but most importantly, allow you to rest easy knowing the problem is solved once and for all!

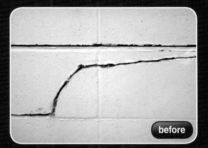
before

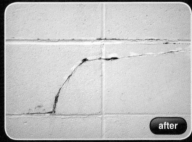
after

before

after

before

after

CHAPTER 5

Sagging Floors Over a Crawl Space
Do the Floors Above Your Crawl Space Seem Bouncy, Soft or Unlevel?

SINK
SETTLE
SAG

► # What Causes Sagging Floors Over a Crawl Space?

Sagging floors are not only a nuisance, but can leave you wondering how much longer the floor will be able to support the weight of everything on it! So what created the problem?

1 *Existing block or brick columns are spaced too far apart.*
When a crawl space is built, block or brick (heck, even sometimes wood) columns are located throughout the crawl space to support the weight of the structure above. If those columns are spaced too far apart, the beam or girder can become overloaded and sag between the columns. When the girder sags, so does the floor above it.

2 *Weakened floor joists and girders due to moisture and wood rot.* Because crawl spaces are often unsealed from the earth, excess moisture and humidity is a problem. And what happens to wood when it has been exposed to moisture and humidity? It begins to rot, get moldy and become weak. Yuck! The weakened girders and floor joists are unable to continue supporting the weight above, and the floor above the crawl space becomes bouncy, soft and may begin to sag.

C5

3 *Existing columns settle due to weak soil.* In previous chapters we've discussed the problems soil can cause, and it's no different here. Weak soil can cause the existing columns in the crawl space to sink or settle, often creating a gap between the top of the column and the bottom of the girder it was supporting. Once the column settles, then the girder sags and the floors above sag. It's a chain reaction.

▶ 'What are the signs? How will I know if I have this problem?'

- Sloping floors, sometimes creating a gap between the floor and interior walls.

- Cracks in interior walls and door frames out of level, caused by a wall sinking along with the floor.

- Gaps between existing columns and girders in the crawl space.

- Shimming between existing columns and girders in the crawl space.

- Evidence of moisture, wood rot, and compression of the floor joists in the crawl space.

Apples & Oranges

CAUTION

▶ Fixing It

What <u>NOT</u> to Have Done... and Why

Concrete Columns

What is it? Concrete footings are poured throughout your crawl space. After the concrete footings cure, concrete blocks are stacked on top of the footings, sometimes with mortar placed between the blocks. After the mortar cures, shims are placed between the uppermost concrete block and the girder.

Why might people choose this? It's a common solution and concrete seems strong.

Why this doesn't work. Not only is this solution time consuming due to all of the waiting for concrete and mortar to cure, but it is also not adjustable. As the concrete column later settles into the soil below, additional shims may need to be added. In other words, this isn't a long term solution. If the existing concrete columns in your crawl space aren't working, why would new ones?

Additional Shimming

What is it? A temporary jack is used to lift the girder to make room for the shims. Shims are then pushed between the existing column and the girder. The temporary jacks are removed.

Why might people choose this? It's cheap and easy.

Why this doesn't work. You get what you pay for. Additional shimming is only a temporary fix, and you will find yourself repairing damages again and again and again.

Try as it may, this little shim cannot prevent your floor from sagging.

Light-duty Jack Post

What is it? A concrete block is laid on top of the soil, and a light-duty jack post is set into place. The light-duty jack post is then tightened to fit against the girder.

Why might people choose this? A light-duty jack post can be purchased at the local hardware store and installed by the homeowner. There's nothing like a do-it-yourself project.

Why this doesn't work. Do you want anything referred to as 'light-duty' stabilizing your sagging floor? Light-duty jack posts can hold very little weight, are difficult to adjust, and don't address the most important problem – the weak foundation soils below.

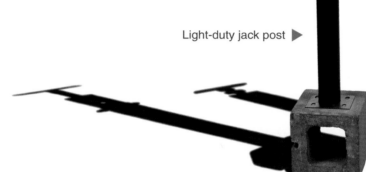

Light-duty jack post ▶   Heavy-duty SmartJack™ ▶

 Side Note

We've heard of do-it-yourself projects, but these homeowners should have left it for the professionals!

Fixing It: *The Smart Solution*

What TO Have Done... and Why

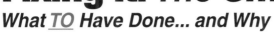

Before

After

The SmartJack™ Crawl Space Stabilizer

What is it? SmartJacks™ are steel support systems used to stabilize and level the girders and floor joists in a crawl space. The heavy-duty system has been laboratory tested to support loads of more than 60,000 lbs, making it the ideal system to stabilize your sagging floor, any walls sitting on top of that floor, and additional loads from the home.

How does it work? To address weak foundation soils, a 2' cube of soil is excavated at each SmartJack™ location. The hole is then filled with either concrete or engineered fill that consists of tightly-compacted crushed stone. A pre-cast concrete base is set into place and leveled on top of or within the engineered fill. Next, a high strength, galvanized steel column is cut to the appropriate height for your crawl space. The steel column and components are assembled and connected to the girder, and the SmartJack™ system is tightened into place. The girder and floor joists are immediately stabilized, and lifting the above floors and walls back to level can be attempted.

When to use it. SmartJacks™ should be used when you want to accomplish the following:

- Best opportunity to lift the above floors and walls back to their original position.

- Engineered footing transfers the load beyond the troubled soils.

- Can be installed in conjunction with a crawl space liner.

- Restores property value.

- ***Problem solved once and for all!***

When *NOT* to use it. If the floor above is extremely damaged and weak.

Why it's the best. The SmartJack™ is super strong *(supports loads of more than 60,000 lbs.)*, is adjustable, and is the ONLY solution that addresses problem soils.

TECH TALK — This is a **BIG** IDEA!

The Bulb of Influence

The *'Bulb of Influence.'* Doesn't it just sound important? Well, it is. This is what makes the SmartJack™ work and different than other possible options for repair. We are often asked, 'Why should only a 2' cube be excavated at each SmartJack™ location? Wouldn't it be better to go deeper?' Here's how the engineering works: at a depth of twice the bearing width, bearing stresses dissipate to approximately 10% of those at the bearing surface. What?! In other words, the SmartJack™ pre-cast concrete base is 12" wide. This is the bearing width. Two times 12" is 24" or two feet. So, at the bottom of the 2' hole, the pressure that was being exerted at the pre-cast base is reduced down to only 10% of what it was. Even if the soil at the bottom of the excavated hole isn't all that strong, you can be assured that the *'Bulb of Significant Stress Influence'* has already been distributed within the crushed stone footing. Any system that does not address this will not be a long-term solution.

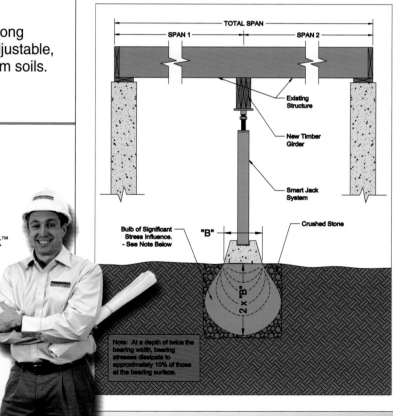

TOTAL SPAN

SPAN 1 — SPAN 2

Existing Structure

New Timber Girder

Smart Jack System

Bulb of Significant Stress Influence. - See Note Below

"B"

Crushed Stone

2 x "B"

Note: At a depth of twice the bearing width, bearing stresses dissipate to approximately 10% of those at the bearing surface.

Crawl Space Encapsulation

You'll Love This!

Dirt Crawl Spaces – A Housing Epidemic

Besides dry soils causing settling of your floors and high humidity causing mold and rot and all the fun that goes with it, dirt crawl spaces cause other problems, which can all be corrected at the same time in one project.

Let's review this more than significant problem briefly...

Exposed earth under a wood floor. You don't have to be a rocket scientist to figure out that damp earth will contribute moisture into your home. And when the earth dries out, soils can shrink and settle and take the piers that hold up your floor with them.

Groundwater leaks. Often, builders pay little attention to keeping a crawl space dry (Hey, it's not very deep so it shouldn't leak, right?) so when it rains hard, they leak. And oftentimes, crawl space foundation walls are made from porous hollow block – God's gift to waterproofing contractors.

Vents. Vents are supposed to let the moisture out. But they don't. The house has a suction at the lower levels as warm air rises in the house. This sucks air in at all the vents. In winter, you have freezing cold air under your feet! Not so good for the heating bill or comfort. *Read on...*

Mold. In the summer, the vents let in warm humid air. The crawl space is cool because it's underground. When the warm humid air contacts the cool surfaces, you get condensation all over everything – and mold is having a party. Critters love damp places, too. And mold doesn't help the health of the occupants or your home's resale value very much these days.

What's downstairs is upstairs. As the house sucks air from bottom to top it takes moisture, mold spores, odors, etc. upstairs to greet you. The humid air also raises your air conditioning costs in a significant way.

What's good about a vented dirt crawl space? *Nothing.*

Help! My existing joists and girders are moldy and weak! Can I still use a SmartJack™?

Yes. Either new joists or girders can be installed, or new lumber can be 'sistered' to each side of the joist or girder. 'Sistering' is the practice of screwing new lumber alongside a structurally compromised girder or floor joist. BUT, you MUST get the mold problem under control. Read on to learn about crawl space encapsulation systems.

Steps to Fixing a Vented Dirt Crawl Space

1 Fix any groundwater problem...

with an interior drainage system and a 'SmartSump' designed just for crawl spaces.

2 Isolate the house from the earth...

with the CleanSpace® Encapsulation System. Like a heavy pool liner, it seals up all the walls, and across the floor. This will help to keep the crawl space dry above the CleanSpace® liner, and help prevent the soils from over drying *(shrinking)* beneath the CleanSpace® liner.

3 Seal all outside air leaks...

including vents! Keep unconditioned outside air out! This does wonders for the overall air leakage rate of your house. Studies show that by taking these measures you can lower your heating and cooling costs by up to 20%!

4 Dehumidify

Not just any machine will do. A SaniDry CSB Crawl Space Air System is a high-performance machine perfect for the application. Mold doesn't stand a chance, and your floor joists and girders will not be further weakened.

BEFORE: One of several cracks in the drywall.

AFTER: Drywall cracks closed.

BEFORE: Gap between the wall & ceiling.

AFTER: Gap between the wall & ceiling eliminated.

SmartJacks™ under supplemental beam within the crawlspace.

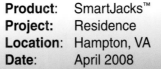

Product: SmartJacks™
Project: Residence
Location: Hampton, VA
Date: April 2008

CASE STUDY

C5

PROBLEM

The home is a two-story framed structure built in 1983. The homeowner had observed the typical warning signs of foundation settlement for some time, including drywall cracks, doors and windows that did not fully open or close, uneven floors and noticeable separation between the ceiling and the walls. They previously tried to remedy the problem by having the center beam replaced, as well as continual cosmetic repair to the drywall cracks. Upon inspection from within the crawl space, JES determined that the center beam and masonry piers had settled, causing the middle of the home to drop. Additionally, the floor joists were over-spanned and bowing. The high-humidity environment of the crawl space likely also contributed to the sagging floor joist condition.

SOLUTION

JES remedied the problem by installing five SmartJacks™ to lift and stabilize the center beam of the house. Five additional SmartJacks™ were installed beneath a supplemental beam to support the sagging floor joists. The moisture and mold issue was corrected by installing a CleanSpace® Crawl Space Encapsulation System and SaniDry™ dehumidification and air filtration system.

RESULTS

The installation of the SmartJacks™ and supplemental beam lifted the house and stabilized it. Drywall cracks closed, and the wall and ceiling gap was eliminated. Doors and windows that were cracked and not functioning properly are now in correct working order. Floors are level with bowing and bouncing eliminated.

TESTIMONIAL

'I have had these structural issues with my home for many years and have tried different ways to fix the problems. The JES inspector took time to analyze the issues and develop a cost effective and efficient way to correct the problem once and for all. As a retired professional engineer myself, I am impressed with the results and am confident of their long term effects.' – Homeowner

PROJECT SUMMARY
Installing Contractor: JES Construction
Products Installed: 10 SmartJacks™, 1,437 sq. ft. of CleanSpace®, 1 SaniDry™ Model CSB, supplemental beam

CASE STUDY

Product: SmartJacks™
Project: Sacred Heart Church Renovation
Location: Omaha, NE
Date: May 2009

Sacred Heart Church is a historical landmark.

CHALLENGE

The Sacred Heart Church is a stone and brick structure that was built in 1897 and named to the National Register of Historic Places in 1983. In 2009, a major renovation project began at the church. In order to refurbish and paint vaulted ceilings throughout the church, scaffolding had to be erected atop the existing structural floor system. The weight of the scaffolding, construction equipment and other construction materials, required that a supplemental support system be installed within the crawl space to carry the additional load. A preliminary design consisted of poured concrete footings with masonry columns, which was going to be difficult and costly to install within the tight confines of the crawl space.

Structural fill and pre-cast footings are installed.

SOLUTION

The General Contractor for the project called Thrasher Basement Systems, Inc. to discuss potential alternative support systems to use in the crawl space. Thrasher recommended the use of the Foundation Supportworks SmartJack™ System, a supplemental support system designed specifically for crawl space applications. Some of the SmartJack™ system design features include: a compacted crushed stone base, a precast concrete footing, a 3½ inch diameter steel column, and an adjustable threaded rod to set the height. All of the steel components are galvanized and zinc-plated for corrosion protection. After reviewing the technical information, the architect approved the use of SmartJacks™ for the project. The SmartJack™ system was the ideal solution because of the quick installation time and major cost reduction versus other options. In total, twenty-two (22) SmartJacks™ were installed in three days, allowing the renovation project to remain on schedule.

SmartJack™ is installed and plumbed.

SmartJacks™ provide supplemental support to existing beams.

PROJECT SUMMARY

Certified Installer: Thrasher Basement Systems, Inc.
Products Installed: (22) SmartJacks™

SmartJack™ installation is completed.

What a Difference!

SmartJacks™ can do more than stabilize.
Floor can be brought back to level, cracks in
drywall can close, and you can sleep at night
knowing this problem is gone… *for good*!

before

after

before

after

before

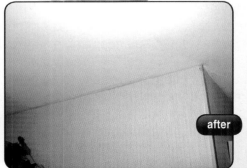

after

CHAPTER 6

Preventing Problems *Before* They Start – *New Construction*

This is a **BIG IDEA!**

▶ In areas with problem soil, forward-thinking engineers and contractors are building homes with helical piers (also called helical piles) in order to address settlement problems before they start.

In many urban and suburban areas, the 'good' land is developed quickly, leaving only those less desirable properties. In many cases, this land was not previously used to build on because the soils weren't strong enough to support a structure. As cities grow and land values increase, builders and developers look for ways to utilize all of the available space. In other cases, lack of space isn't the issue at all. Sometimes people simply want to build a home in a certain area because of its beauty, landscape or proximity to something like a lake or scenic view. No matter what the reason, helical piers can be installed before construction to ensure you never have to worry about foundation settlement problems.

▶ How Could This Benefit You?

- No annoying and expensive ongoing fixes, such as drywall patches and tuck-pointing.

- No throwing money down the drain on unplanned repair expenses that creep up on you – both cosmetic and structural.

- Peace of mind – your dream home won't become a nightmare!

▶ How Does It Work?

After the footings are dug for a new home, helical piers can be installed. Using small construction equipment, helical piers are mechanically screwed into the ground until they reach competent, load-bearing soil. Piers can be installed to support both the foundations and the floor slabs. After the piers have been installed to the proper depths, the concrete footings and walls of the home are poured around the piers. The tops of the piers are actually cast right into the concrete foundation which effectively transfers the weight of the home down to the bottoms of the piers, deep in solid ground. Installing new construction helical piers is a surefire method to defend against future settlement of a home.

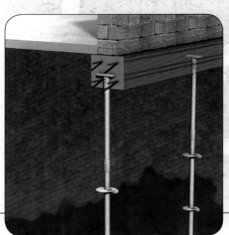

CASE STUDY

Product: Helical Piers
Project: New Home Construction
Location: Calgary, Alberta • Canada
Date: August 2008

Helical piers installed.

PROBLEM

A couple purchased a building lot for their dream home, only to discover that it had some features that stymied previous property owners and builders from using traditional foundation construction methods. A soil investigation found competent bearing soils some 14 feet below grade, coupled with a water table at 4 feet. A deep excavation to the suitable bearing soils was not possible with such a high water table, so the homeowners found themselves seeking an alternative foundation support system.

Helical piers installed.

SOLUTION

Basement Systems Calgary, working with a local structural engineer, recommended new construction helical piers to effectively transfer the design loads of the home to the deep suitable soil without requiring excavation. The structural design of the home then included foundation walls as structural grade beams, and pier supported structural floor slabs.

Walls being formed with reinforcing steel.

RESULTS

The foundations and structural slabs for both the house and the attached garage are now supported by soils up to 35 feet below grade. With a solid foundation, the homeowners were then able to build their dream home with confidence.

TESTIMONIAL

"We have our new home as a result of the efforts of Basement Systems Calgary who went the extra mile with the municipal planning authorities. We are confident that our home will be on solid footing for a long time to come." – Homeowner

Helical pier caps formed & area ready for structural steel.

PROJECT SUMMARY

Certified Pier Installer: Basement Systems Calgary
Products Installed: (77) Helical Piers, 2 7/8-inch diameter with 10/12 lead section, installed to depths up to 35 feet, 40 kip capacity

TECH TALK

Side Note

Is My Lot a Problem Spot?

You may be asking yourself, "How do I know if I'm building on a problem lot?" If you or your builder are not sure what the soils are like under your future home, the best option is to contact a local geotechnical engineer. Geotechnical engineers specialize in engineering behaviors of soil, and they can conduct a soil investigation at your property. To do this, a soil sample is extracted from the ground. Once the sample is obtained, an engineer will analyze the soil, determine strength characteristics, and decide whether or not adjustments need to be made to the design of your home's foundation. Performing a soil investigation requires an initial upfront investment, but it can save thousands of dollars in the long run and years of headaches and frustration if a problem does exist. If you're not sure where to find a geotechnical engineer in your area, contact your local Foundation Supportworks dealer, and they can provide you with a list of geotechnical engineering firms.

▶ Supporting Buildings Large & Small

Helical piers have been used to support residential homes for decades, but did you know that engineers and architects specify helical products to support major commercial structures, bridges, cell phone towers and retaining walls as well?

CHAPTER 7

Causes and Signs *of Wall Failure*

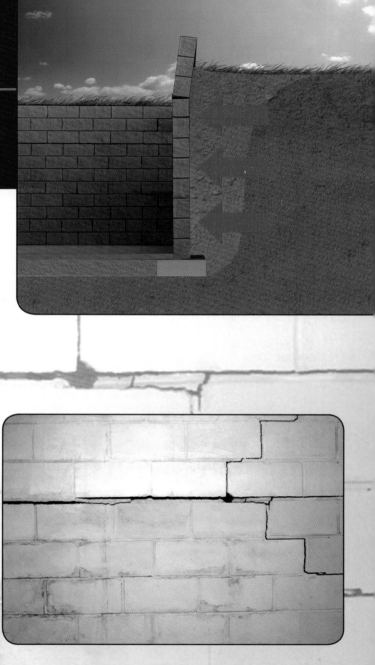

BOW
LEAN
PUSHED-IN

▶ Straight Talk

You may not realize this, but the soil around your home puts a lot of pressure on your foundation walls. The amount of pressure varies depending on the type of soil around the home, the amount of moisture in the soil, and how deep the foundation is under the ground. When you think about it, there is nothing on the inside of the basement walls pushing back (and no, those boxes stacked up against your basement walls don't count!).

When the pressure from outside the basement wall is greater than what the wall can handle, the wall will begin to crack, bow, or push inward. Factors such as expansive clays, hydrostatic pressure, and frost can create too much stress on basement walls and cause them to push inward and even collapse.

What are the common causes of wall failure?

- **Expansive clay soil** – Clay expands and contracts as the amount of moisture in the ground increases and decreases. Have you ever looked at a dirt baseball field during a dry spell and noticed cracks in the dirt? This happens because clay soil shrinks when it's dry. On the other hand, when it rains and clay soil gets wet, it expands. As clay soil expands in size, it puts a lot of pressure on your basement walls. When the pressure becomes more than the wall can handle, the wall will begin to push inward.

- **Hydrostatic Pressure** – What is hydrostatic pressure? It is the pressure exerted by a fluid due to the force of gravity. Simply put, if water is allowed to accumulate within the backfill soils, the water exerts a pressure against the basement wall.

- **Frost** – In areas with cold winter climates, frost can put pressure on a wall and cause it to fail. Frost forces can be extremely powerful and can even lift a foundation up out of the ground. Frost can put literally thousands of pounds of force on a wall and that pressure can create all kinds of problems for basement walls.

How much does moisture affect clay?
These two clay soil samples started out exactly the same – same size, same weight, and same type of clay. The sample on the right was allowed to dry out completely while the sample on the left remained moist. Even the naked eye can see how much clay soil cracks and shrinks as it dries. Imagine how dramatic this is when clay surrounds your entire home!

Hydrostatic pressure exerts added force to the outside of your basement walls.

Side Note

Important!

...en gutters and downspouts are not properly ...tended away from your foundation, added water ...l saturate the soil around your home. When this ...opens, hydrostatic pressure and expansive clay ...il can wreak havoc on your foundation walls. If ...ur downspouts need to be extended, there are ...ective options available to divert water away from ...ur foundation and also increase the cosmetic ...lue of your home. If extending your downspouts ...something your home needs, ask a Foundation ...pportworks representative about your options.

Frost forces at work. ▶

Street Creep

You're probably asking yourself, what in the world is Street Creep? We aren't talking about a bully who lurks around the corner in a dark alley – that's for sure! Street Creep is a real problem that is caused by thermal expansion and contraction of the concrete streets leading to your home.

Concrete expands when it's hot and contracts when cold. Home builders and engineers typically understand that this movement will occur, so they install expansion and control joints to allow for the movement. Because of changes in temperature through the year, expansion and control joints widen in cold winter months and narrow in hot summer months. The problem is that during the winter months, the widened joints in the street can become filled with incompressible material, such as sand and grit. Then, as temperatures rise through the spring and summer months, the concrete expands and either compresses the expansion joints, or pushes against the adjacent concrete slabs with increasing force.

When this expansion takes place, the concrete street elongates. The elongation of a typical block-length concrete street is generally a fraction of an inch per year, but can accumulate to several inches over time.

Three conditions where Street Creep is more likely to affect adjacent properties are shown here.

As the arrows in the diagrams reflect, the elongating concrete street pushes against the concrete driveway, which then pushes against the concrete garage slab or slab-on-grade home. The back of the garage slab often pushes against a basement wall or rear foundation wall, causing wall deflection and cracking. Foundation wall movement can be transferred through the structural framing, generating cracks and distress in other areas of the home as well. Correct diagnosis of Street Creep is essential to providing homeowners with the right solution for their problem.

Reading the Signs
Tell-tale signs of Street Creep include:

1. The existing expansion joints between the street and driveway, and between the driveway and garage slab, are fully compressed. Even if the joint appears wide enough at the surface, the concrete could still be in contact below.
2. The foundation walls on either side of the garage door are pushed inward by the driveway slab.
3. Gaps have formed behind the foundation walls on either side of the garage door as the garage slab is pushed rearward.
4. Basement walls or foundation walls are pushed out by the garage slab.

Solutions such as wall anchors, which will be discussed in the next chapter, have proven to be effective when dealing with the effects of Street Creep.

Home ↑ ↑

Home

Driveway along outside curve of a street

Home

Cul-de-sac Street

Driveway at end of cul-de-sac street

Home ↑

Driveway aligned or nearly aligned with a t-intersection

▶ Is My Wall *Failing?*

Depending on if your walls are built from concrete block or poured concrete, the signs of wall failure will look different.

Some common signs in the case of a <u>block</u> foundation:

- *Horizontal Cracking* – Horizontal cracking near the middle of the wall is one of the first symptoms you will notice in the case of a bowing wall. Horizontal cracks usually start out small and increase in width over time as the soil outside continues to put pressure on the wall.

- *Stair-step Cracking at Corners* – Stair-step cracking at the corners of a bowing wall is another common sign and typically means that the problem is getting worse. As the wall bows more severely in the middle, the corners are held up by adjacent walls, creating the stair-step cracking affect.

- *Pushing-in at the Bottom of the Wall* – If your basement walls begin to push in severely, you may notice the wall sliding inward near the bottom. This happens when the concrete floor in the basement holds the bottom row of blocks in place as the rest of the wall cracks and pushes in.

- *Sliding-in at the Top of the Wall* – Another sign that your wall problem is becoming more severe is when the wall begins to lean in at the top. When the wall begins to slide in at the top, you are dealing with a very serious structural problem because the connection of your foundation wall to the framing of the house has been compromised.

Horizontal Cracking

Stair-step Cracking

Pushing-in at Bottom

Sliding-in at Top

▶ Other Experts Agree!

Important!

A former Chief Appraiser for the U.S. Department of Housing and Urban Development (HUD) said, "Foundation walls usually move first at the weakest point which is at the mid-point of the wall. Walls that have 'bowed' significantly will show 'stairstep' cracking usually at the outside corners. This will require corrective action. The condition will not stabilize. It's a question of how much time remains."

Some common signs in the case of a <u>poured</u> concrete foundation:

- *Leaning-in at the Top of the Wall* – Because poured foundation walls are more rigid than block, they are more likely to lean in at the top rather than bow near the middle like block foundation walls.

- *Diagonal Cracking at Corners* – Diagonal cracking at the corners of a poured wall is a very common sign of wall failure. Because the corners of the wall are supported by adjacent walls, you will see diagonal cracks extending from the bottom corners up toward the top center of the wall.

Leaning In at Top

Diagonal Cracking

Side Note

Other Signs of Bowing, Leaning and Pushed-in Walls...

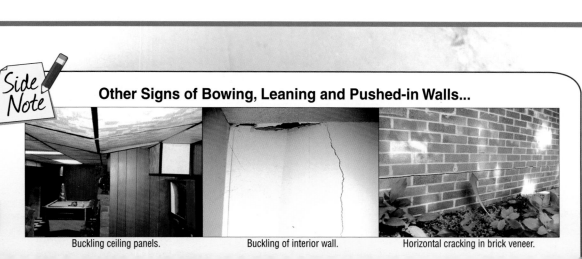

Buckling ceiling panels. Buckling of interior wall. Horizontal cracking in brick veneer.

Omaha World-Herald

THURSDAY, MAY 27, 2004

JAMES R. BURNETT/THE WORLD-HERALD

Mud and rainwater cover the floor of Josh Shannon's Omaha basement after heavy rain Monday caused a wall to collapse.

Basements are muddy mess

Problems don't get better with time, they only get worse.

HOW LONG WILL <u>YOU</u> WAIT
TO FIX YOUR
FAILING BASEMENT WALL?

CHAPTER 8

Solutions to Basement Wall Failure

Giving It To You Straight
...What Works and Doesn't Work in Solving Wall Problems

BOW LEAN PUSHED-IN

The title of this book is "What to have done with your structural problem...and why." As with anything, there are a variety of options, some more effective than others. Shopping for a solution to your failing foundation wall is a serious decision. You need a solution from a trustworthy contractor who will solve your problem...permanently. Unfortunately, the wide variety of options can create confusion, so let's start by eliminating one option that rarely makes sense...in any scenario.

Total Foundation Replacement

What is it? Soil is first excavated from around your foundation walls. Then, the house is jacked up and the floor slab and foundation walls are removed. Finally, the foundation is rebuilt and the soil is replaced.

Why might people choose this? My walls are all cracked up and damaged, so it seems logical to replace them with new ones rather than to repair the existing ones.

Why this doesn't work. This solution is extremely disruptive, expensive, and time consuming, but the real problem is that it doesn't address the issue. The foundation isn't the problem; the soil is the problem. You've simply built a new foundation in the same problem soil, so you can expect that your new foundation walls will break and crack just like the old ones!

CAUTION

▷ Options when *little or no access* is available on the outside of the home:

In some cities and neighborhoods, houses are built very close to one another. If that is the case, here are some options to consider.

Carbon Fiber Straps

What is it? Carbon fiber is a very high tensile strength material that is almost impossible to stretch. Because it doesn't stretch, carbon fiber can be 'glued' to concrete walls *(or block walls)* to keep them from bending or bowing inward. Carbon fiber straps have become a fairly common method for reinforcing basement walls and if installed properly, they can effectively hold the center of the wall in place.

How does it work? Carbon fiber installation begins with the wall being 'scarified' or ground down to create a rough surface on the wall. Then, an epoxy glue is applied to the wall, and the carbon fiber strap is adhered. Once installed, the carbon fiber straps resist further bending of the wall.

When to use it. Carbon fiber straps are a reasonable repair option if the wall is bowing in the middle and hasn't started to slide in at the bottom or lean in at the top. Because carbon fiber installations don't require any outside digging or use of large equipment inside the home, they are also viable when there is limited access inside the basement or on the exterior of the home.

When not to use it. Carbon fiber straps should NOT be used if your basement walls have started to slide in at the bottom or lean in at the top. Since carbon fiber straps are glued to the wall and are not typically anchored to anything at the top or at the bottom, the wall could continue to tip or slide in. Even if the straps are connected at the top of the wall, the force on the wall would then be transferred to the upper floor framing, which may not be designed for that specific load application or magnitude. Carbon fiber straps cannot straighten a wall, so if this is your goal, carbon fibers are not the best choice.

CAUTION

Wall with carbon fiber strap sliding in at the bottom.

Steel Beams

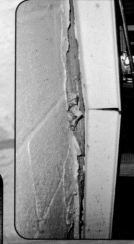

What is it? Steel I-beams are considered an 'old school' method used by contractors who have a minimal amount of experience fixing basement walls. Unfortunately, because I-beams are relatively easy to come by, many contractors with little or no foundation repair experience have installed them over the years, sometimes with negative results.

How does it work? Most I-beam installations begin by standing a beam up against the basement wall. Then, the beam is connected to the wood floor joists at the top of the wall and the concrete floor at the bottom.

Pressure on floor joists can damage wood framing.

Why might people choose this? Many times homeowners don't know who to call when they have a foundation problem and they may talk to a contractor who doesn't have much experience in dealing with foundation problems. Because most contractors don't have specialized knowledge and training in foundation repair and also don't have access to a sophisticated line of products, they are forced to make up a solution using what is available to them.

Why this doesn't work. When I-beams are installed, the soil pressure *(or load)* on the wall is transferred through the beam to the wood floor joists above. Since the pressure from the soil was more than what the concrete wall could handle, what do you think can happen when that pressure is transferred to your wood floor joists if not done properly? Yup – cracking, buckling and other damages to your wood floor framing can occur. For this reason, few qualified contractors still consider this the best option for wall repair. **BEWARE** of those that do!

Steel beams get rusty and create an unattractive look.

CAUTION

More floor joist damages.

▶ 'I don't have space on the outside of my home, but these options don't sound good to me.'

Well, the fact is that sometimes homeowners don't have access on the outside of their home, and they still have a problem that needs to be dealt with. While we always recommend utilizing systems that can anchor the wall and stabilize it without relying on the floor joists for support, sometimes anchoring systems can't be used. Because of this, Foundation Supportworks has developed a system called the PowerBrace™.

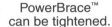

PowerBrace™ can be tightened.

PowerBrace™ System

The PowerBrace™ is a patented system that is designed to stabilize failing basement walls and allow for potential straightening over time. Here are some benefits of the PowerBrace™ System over other common I-beam systems:

- Can be tightened to allow for improvement of the wall over time
- Beam and components are zinc coated so they won't rust
- Neat and clean appearance in the basement
- Professionally installed
- No outside excavation required

Now we're the first to admit, the PowerBrace™ is an I-beam system and could cause problems to wood floor joists if they're not designed to resist the additional forces from the wall. However, as we've mentioned, sometimes property line issues require that these options be used. Because variations in building design and construction materials are common, we recommend that PowerBrace™ applications be reviewed by a qualified professional to ensure that the flooring system can handle the additional load. We also only work with high quality contractors to make certain that an appropriate system is recommended for your home. When installed properly and in the right application, there is not another I-beam system available that offers the benefits of the PowerBrace™.

Large equipment is required to install helical anchors.

▷ Options when access *is* available on the outside of the home:

Helical Anchor Systems

What is it? Helical anchors have been used to stabilize foundation and retaining walls for years and have proven to be quite effective. Helical anchors are designed like a screw and can be mechanically advanced through the soil using a large machine called a drive head. Helical anchors are widely accepted by engineers and architects and are used to support commercial structures all around the world. Some residential contractors also use these anchors to stabilize bowing basement walls.

How does it work? When installing helical anchors in a basement, the first thing that has to be done is to cut a big hole in the wall. Then, a hydraulic motor is taken into the basement and used to advance the anchor into the ground. The hole in the foundation wall is then filled with concrete, and a steel plate connects the helical anchor to the wall.

When _to_ use it. Helical anchors are a good option for anchoring a wall when lots of space is available in the basement and water leakage isn't a concern. An important benefit of helical anchors is that they don't rely on the framing of the house for support. They can also be used on walls that are bowing, tipping in at the top, and are pushing in at the bottom, unlike some other options.

Example of a leaking, ineffective helical anchor installation.

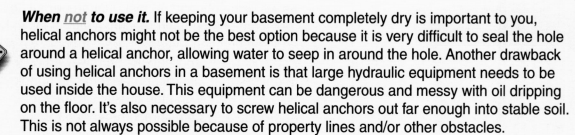

CAUTION

When _not_ to use it. If keeping your basement completely dry is important to you, helical anchors might not be the best option because it is very difficult to seal the hole around a helical anchor, allowing water to seep in around the hole. Another drawback of using helical anchors in a basement is that large hydraulic equipment needs to be used inside the house. This equipment can be dangerous and messy with oil dripping on the floor. It's also necessary to screw helical anchors out far enough into stable soil. This is not always possible because of property lines and/or other obstacles.

Wall Anchor Systems

What is it? Wall anchor systems have been used successfully since the late 1970's to stabilize foundation and retaining walls. These systems consist of heavy-duty, galvanized steel earth anchors that are embedded into the soil out away from the foundation wall. They are connected to steel wall plates with galvanized anchoring rods. Wall anchors have proven over many years to be both an effective and economical repair solution. Once installed, wall anchors will hold walls in their current position without any further adjustment. A unique and important benefit of wall anchor systems is their ability to be tightened during dry periods, allowing for improvement and straightening of the wall over time. In fact, in 1992, wall anchor systems were identified by a Chief Appraiser for the U.S. Department of Housing and Urban Development as the most effective means of stabilizing bowing foundation walls.

How does it work? Wall anchors are installed by auguring or digging a hole into the soil away from your foundation. A steel rod is drilled through a 1" hole in your basement wall and is connected to an earth anchor that is seated deep within the augured hole. A low-profile wall plate placed on the interior of your basement wall is secured to the rod. The augured hole is backfilled and sod is replaced. Once all components of the wall anchor system are connected and tightened, your basement wall is permanently stabilized.

When to use it. Wall Anchors are the most versatile wall repair method because they can be used to stabilize walls with a variety of problems such as bowing walls, walls that are tipping in at the top, and walls that are pushing in at the bottom. Wall anchors are installed independently of the floor systems of a home and are a good choice for the following reasons:

- Best opportunity to straighten the wall over time
- Can fix severe problems such as leaning walls and walls sliding in at the bottom
- Can be installed around obstacles on the wall such as pipes, conduits, vanities, sinks, toilets, etc.
- Minimal disturbance from installation
- Quick installation
- Restores property value
- Problem solved once and for all

When not to use it. In order for a wall anchor system to work effectively, several feet of access is needed on the outside of your home. In areas where homes are only a few feet apart, wall anchors are not a valid option. If this is the case for you, another wall repair option will be required.

▶ **Wall Anchors:** *Why Foundation Supportworks' Geo-Lock™ Anchors Are the Best*

With any foundation repair project, the most important thing is to have an experienced contractor who can fix the problem. Foundation Supportworks is the largest supplier of wall anchor systems in North America – <u>BY FAR</u>, so you can rest assured that your anchors will be installed by an experienced company. Besides having the most experienced installation contractors, Geo-Lock™ anchors also have some unique design features:

- **Multiple Earth Anchor Sizes** - Geo-Lock™ earth anchors are sized to perform in various soil types and have a bearing surface of up to 480 square inches. Other anchor systems, such as helical anchors, have a typical bearing surface of only 43 square inches. In other words, Geo-Lock™ anchors can have 10 times more contact with the soil, resulting in more holding power in weak soils!

- **Protective Rod End Caps** – All Geo-Lock™ anchors are installed with a cap that covers the rod on the inside of the basement. These caps not only create a neat and clean look, but also protect from any burs or sharp edges on the end of the anchor rod.

- **Anchor Covers** - The patent-pending Hide-A-Way™ Anchor Covers offered by Foundation Supportworks are the perfect solution for anchor installations in both finished and unfinished basements. The removable Hide-A-Way™ Anchor Covers conceal your anchors while still allowing for periodic tightening of the system. Other advantages include:

  - Snap-on design allows homeowners future access to the tightening bolts so that further adjustments can be made, if desired.
  - Maintains a neat and clean look in your basement living space.
  - Sleek, low-profile design fits tight against the wall so they don't protrude into your valuable living space.

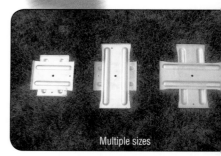

Multiple sizes

Protective rod end

Before   After

Hide-A-Way™ Anchor Covers

What Keeps the Anchors From Pulling Through the Wall?

Wall anchors can be tightened periodically throughout dry seasons to slowly pull walls back to a straight position. But what keeps the plates from pulling through the wall when they're tightened? Geo-Lock™ Wall Anchors are tightened to a specific amount of torque that is easily measured and correlates to a force that is easily handled by the strength of the wall and the passive resistance of the soil on the outside of the wall *(backfill soils)*. In addition, there are literally hundreds of thousands of anchors that have been installed throughout North America that provide an ongoing testimony to the effectiveness of the Geo-Lock™ system.

Are Wall Anchors a 'One Size Fits All' Approach?

Competitors who know just a little might argue that wall anchors are a 'one size fits all' approach to repairing basement walls. Geo-Lock™ Wall Anchors have been designed to extend a minimum distance of twelve feet out from the foundation wall to prevent the load from the anchor being transferred back to the wall. There are several factors that need to be considered when designing an effective wall anchor system such as height of the wall, height of the backfill, vertical placement of the wall plate, type of soil, and strength of soil. By assuming some of the worst possible soil conditions, and assuming backfill heights up to eight feet tall, you can be assured that an anchor length of twelve feet will be adequate. In special circumstances or when backfill heights are greater than eight feet, the anchor length can be easily extended. Adjustments can readily be made to the wall anchor spacing, anchor rod length, and size of the earth anchor to ensure the anchors will provide adequate holding capacity in almost any soil condition.

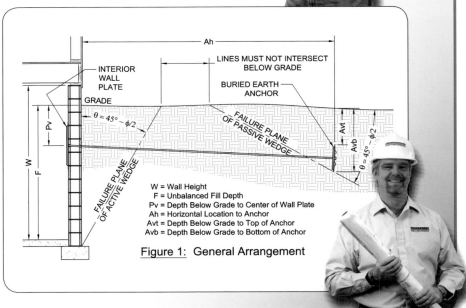

W = Wall Height
F = Unbalanced Fill Depth
Pv = Depth Below Grade to Center of Wall Plate
Ah = Horizontal Location to Anchor
Avt = Depth Below Grade to Top of Anchor
Avb = Depth Below Grade to Bottom of Anchor

<u>Figure 1:</u> General Arrangement

What if I Want My Wall Straight _NOW?_

In some cases, basement walls have leaned or bowed in severely and are in a dangerously unstable condition. Other times homeowners want to straighten their walls right away so they can finish their basement. Regardless of the reason, basement walls can be excavated and straightened immediately rather than waiting to tighten the walls periodically. Sometimes straightening the wall is the best option, and it can be done at a fraction of the cost of replacing the foundation.

Leaning concrete walls.

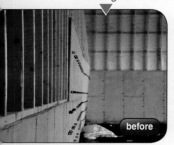

Wall bowing inward due to soil saturation and expansion.

► Wall Anchor Application Chart

You'll Love This! $

Choose the Right System for <u>YOU</u> Based on Your Situation and Goals

Condition \ Solution	Removal & Replacement	Carbon Fiber Straps	I-beams	Helical Anchors	Geo-Lock™ Wall Anchors
Installation Usually Completed in One Day	✗	✓	✓	✗	✓
Does Not Have Problems with Leaking	✓	✓	✓	✗	✓
Does Not Rely on Floor System for Support	✓	✗	✗	✓	✓
Stabilizes Walls that are Bowing In at the Center of the Wall	✗	✓	✓	✓	✓
Will Keep the Wall From Tipping/Leaning In at the Top of the Wall	✗	✗	✓	✓	✓
Will Keep the Wall From Sliding In at the Bottom of the Wall	✗	✗	✓	✓	✓
Limited Disturbance to Lawn and Landscaping	✗	✓	✓	✓	✓
Can Straighten Wall Over Time Without Excavating	✗	✗	✗	✓	✓
Can be Installed in Areas With Close Property Lines	✓	✓	✓	✗	✗
Can be Installed when Interior Access is Limited	✗	✓	✓	✗	✓
Can Easily Avoid Obstructions on Basement Walls such as Pipes, Wires and Plumbing Lines	✗	✗	✗	✓	✓

Anchor rod is driven out through the wall.

The earth anchor is installed deep within the soil.

Wall plates are attached and system is tightened.

Installation is complete with Hide-A-Way™ Anchor Covers.

Product: Geo-Lock™ Wall Anchors and Hide-A-Way™ Anchor Covers
Project: Residence
Location: Lincoln, NE
Date: November 2009

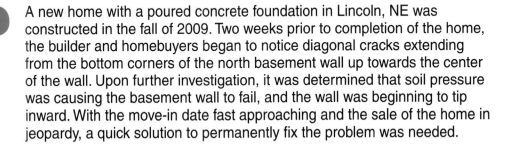

CASE STUDY

C8

PROBLEM

A new home with a poured concrete foundation in Lincoln, NE was constructed in the fall of 2009. Two weeks prior to completion of the home, the builder and homebuyers began to notice diagonal cracks extending from the bottom corners of the north basement wall up towards the center of the wall. Upon further investigation, it was determined that soil pressure was causing the basement wall to fail, and the wall was beginning to tip inward. With the move-in date fast approaching and the sale of the home in jeopardy, a quick solution to permanently fix the problem was needed.

SOLUTION

After reviewing their options, the builder and the homebuyers decided to have Thrasher Basement Systems install eight (8) Geo-Lock™ Wall Anchors to stabilize the foundation wall and potentially straighten the wall over time. The installation began by embedding earth anchors deep into stable soil 12' out from the failing wall. Then, earth anchors were connected to wall plates on the inside of the wall with threaded steel rods. To further enhance the look of the home, Hide-A-Way™ Anchor Covers were installed over the wall plates. This provided a neat-and-clean look, while allowing the homeowners to continue to tighten the anchors and straighten the wall over time. Installation of the Geo-Lock™ system was ideal in this case because the one-day installation allowed the buyers to move into their new home on the scheduled date. Best of all, the engineered system provided a long-term warranty and peace-of-mind to the new homeowners.

PROJECT SUMMARY

Installing Contractor: Thrasher Basement Systems
Products Installed: (8) Foundation Supportworks Geo-Lock™ Wall Anchors and (8) Hide-A-Way™ Anchor Covers

CHAPTER 9
What Do I Do Now?...

To get your foundation fixed permanently, you'll need to know exactly what YOU need at your home. Finding out is simple – contact your local Foundation Supportworks dealer if you haven't already. You can find your local dealer by visiting www.FoundationSupportworks.com.

You can expect a trained foundation repair expert to come out to your home for a complete inspection, consultation, and a free written proposal including cost. Then you can have the work completed and feel good knowing your foundation is strong and stable again.

▶ *Who is Foundation Supportworks?*

Foundation Supportworks is a leading designer, manufacturer, and distributor of foundation stabilization systems for new and existing residential, commercial and industrial structures. While the words 'integrity' and 'quality' are used by most these days, Foundation Supportworks is a special company where these virtues are reflected in everyday decision making and behavior by our talented and dedicated staff and network of independent dealers throughout North America.

Foundation Supportworks' products are professionally manufactured with the utmost care & quality.

Foundation Supportworks has both structural and geotechnical engineers in-house.

Foundation Supportworks is the only manufacturer with both structural and geotechnical engineers in-house. Our engineers not only focus on product design and quality assurance, but also provide technical support to engineers, architects, building departments, and general contractors local to the projects. Our engineers are true authorities in the field.

The Foundation Supportworks dealer network consists of nearly 100 of the most experienced structural repair contractors in North America. Training our dealers is a vital function at our company, and we hold more than 15 major training events per year for our dealers and their employees.

Foundation Supportworks places a high emphasis on training.

Omaha, Nebraska

Seymour, Connecticut

Foundation Supportworks has major facilities in Omaha, Nebraska and Seymour, Connecticut, and continues to grow.

Dave Thrasher is a second generation foundation specialist who trains and develops foundation contractors throughout North America as the Director of Business Development for Foundation Supportworks. Dave grew up in the foundation business and began working on an installation crew for his father's foundation repair company at the age of fourteen. Dave has installed hundreds of foundation repair systems with his own hands, which gives him a unique level of understanding about foundation problems and their solutions.

Dave graduated with honors from Concordia University Wisconsin where he obtained a bachelor's degree in Business Communications and Marketing. He was also honored at Concordia with the 'Most Outstanding Student of the Year' award. After earning his degree, Dave worked in various marketing and sales positions for two Fortune 1000 companies, Werner Enterprises and Union Pacific.

Dave is a nationally recognized expert at diagnosing foundation issues, and consults with contractors and homeowners every day to develop solutions to foundation problems. He is a frequent contributor to various publications as well as being a speaker at industry conferences.

Dave was born and raised in Omaha, NE and continues to reside there today with his wife Tabitha and two children, Addison and Landon. Outside of work he enjoys softball, golf, fishing and spending time with his family. Dave is also an active member of his church where he volunteers and serves as a leader in several areas of ministry.

Amanda Harrington has been active in the foundation repair industry since early 2007 and currently serves as Director of Training and Development for Foundation Supportworks, Inc. Amanda graduated with honors from Doane College in Crete, Nebraska with a Bachelor of Arts degree in Corporate Communication with an emphasis in Training and Development.

With over twelve years of experience in senior-level training roles in various industries, Amanda has conducted trainings in more than ten countries on five continents. She has been honored with two Best Practices awards by the Human Resources Association of the Midlands for her work in creating education-based materials and programs. Amanda has also been featured in the Working Women's section of *Today's Omaha Woman* magazine as a young, professional female making an impact in the Omaha business community.

Amanda has consulted on and contributed to articles in various industry publications and regularly speaks at industry events. She is an expert in researching and writing curriculum, developing education-based materials, and coaching other training facilitators in the areas of management, sales, marketing and installation.

In her spare time, Amanda enjoys spending time with her husband, John; daughter, Moyra; and step-children, Jean-Luc and Stryder. She has a passion for travel, enjoys reading, movies, music, gardening, antiquing, and spending time with friends.

Larry Janesky is an authority on basement repair and building effective businesses that serve homeowners well. In 1982 he began five years of self employment as a carpenter and builder before founding Basement Systems Inc. in 1987. Today, Basement Systems is the largest network of waterproofing and crawl space repair contractors in the world. Larry has taken personal responsibility for repairing 29,000 basements over 24 years through his local installation business in Connecticut. Larry is also president of Total Basement Finishing, a leading network of finishing contractors, and Dr. Energy Saver, a network of energy conservation contractors.

Along with his friend Greg Thrasher, Larry co-founded Foundation Supportworks in Omaha, Nebraska. Larry has trained thousands of talented, dedicated basement repair contractors and their employees in the last 20 years. He holds 27 patents.

Larry is the author of 7 books including 'Dry Basement Science', 'Crawl Space Science', 'Basement Finishing Science', 'Saving Energy and Money at Home', and 'The Highest Calling – An Inspirational Novel About Business and Life, Struggle and Success.' He writes a daily blog called 'Think Daily', received by over 7000 people each morning.

Larry enjoys seeing everyone around him succeed. His mission is to make the world a better place for homeowners, employees, businesspeople and society in general, by helping build successful businesses that serve all effectively.

He lives in Middlebury, Connecticut with his wife Wendy, his son Tanner, and daughters Chloe and Autumn. He enjoys outdoor activities with his family and is a passionate motocross rider.

Trusted Partners

Foundation Supportworks is 1 of 5 sister companies within an expansive network. All companies are industry leaders in their respective fields. Much like **Foundation Repair Science**, each has developed an informational book about problems homeowners face and their options for solutions. Visit their websites and request a free copy of their books, compliments of our network.

Basement Systems®, Inc.
Basement waterproofing

BasementSystems.com

Dry Basement Science
What to Have Done... and Why

CleanSpace®
Crawl space repair

CleanSpaceSystem.com

Crawl Space Science
What to Have Done... and Why

Total Basement Finishing™
Basement finishing

TotalBasementFinishing.com

Basement Finishing Science
What to Have Done... and Why

Dr. Energy Saver™
Home energy contracting

DrEnergySaver.com

Saving Energy and $ at Home
What to Have Done... and Why

Acknowledgements

We would like to acknowledge the following people
and companies for their contributions:

Our spouses and children who allow us to share our work,
stories and experiences with them.

JES Construction, Peak Structural, J&D Basement Systems – Northwest,
Basement Systems of Calgary, Frontier Basement Systems, Thrasher
Basement Systems, Advanced Basement Systems, Woods Basement
Systems, Terra Firma Foundation Systems, Quality 1st Basement Systems,
Sure-Dry Basement Systems, Insta-Dry Basement Systems, and Foundation
Recovery Systems for photos and case studies.

Thiele Geotech, Inc. and Terracon Consultants, Inc. in Omaha, Nebraska for
use of soil samples and access to laboratories and equipment.

Greg Thrasher, Dan Thrasher, Tiffany Seevers, Jeff Kortan, Don Deardorff
and Kyle Olson for their great editing.

Scott Clark for layout and design.

The staff at our company, Foundation Supportworks, Inc. and our many
dealers who are helping to make the world a better place
by fixing foundation problems every day.